WHAT'S YOUR
BIO STRATEGY?

How to Prepare Your Business
for Synthetic Biology

D1572171

25 Trailblazers Interviewed

JOHN CUMBERS, PhD & KARL SCHMIEDER, MS/MFA

What's Your Bio Strategy?

How to Prepare Your Business for Synthetic Biology
25 Trailblazers Interviewed

By John Cumbers, PhD & Karl Schmieder, MS/MFA

PULP BIO BOOKS

What's Your Bio Strategy

E-book design by Camelia Gherib and Matías Baldanza.
Book design by Matías Baldanza.
Illustrations by Edina Pusok.

Pulp Bio Books | China | Indonesia | U.K. | USA
Pulpbiobooks.com
What's Your Bio Strategy?

Printed and bound in the United States of America.
Edition ISBN hardback: 978-0-9993136-1-9
Edition ISBN eBook: 978-0-9993136-2-6
Edition ISBN trade paperback: 978-0-9993136-0-2

FIRST EDITION

Biology is programmable.

Synthetic biology is impacting business right now.

Businesses without a bio strategy are being disrupted.

1, Darlene Solomon   CTO Agilent

CONTENTS

Section 3.
Biological Escape Velocity 99

INTRODUCTION

IF YOU'RE LIKE MANY PEOPLE, you wake up in the morning, stretch out on your cotton sheets, and reach for your smartphone.

After you check the time, you slip into a clean pair of jeans and walk to the kitchen where you grind your coffee, place it in a paper filter, and pour water over it.

You drink your coffee while eating a breakfast cereal with milk. Then, you get in your car and drive to work.

During each one of those steps, biotechnology touched your life.

The sheets you woke up on were made from cotton genetically engineered to attack the boll weevils and bollworms that used to ravage cotton fields. Before biotechnology, farmers used to spray their fields with toxic pesticides every three days for boll weevils and every five days for boll worms.

The plastic cover on your smartphone might have been created from a bioplastic. Bioplastics are created from sustainable sources, such as vegetable oils and biomass. They are biodegradable. Since they are not petrochemical-based, derived from non-renewable sources, bioplastics will not contribute to the floating islands of plastic currently predicted to outweigh the biomass of all fish by 2030. Nor will they contribute to climate change, as the carbon dioxide used to create them came from the air, not from oil.

The jeans you're wearing were washed using enzymes (biological catalysts) that were genetically modified to help break down organic materials in cold water. By washing in cold water, you're using less electricity and emitting fewer greenhouse gases.

The coffee filter you used was bleached using enzymes that reduce the amount of chlorine and energy used in manufacturing. Coffee filters, like many other types of paper, used to be bleached using sodium hypochlorite, which is bad for the environment. Using biotechnology eliminates that environmental risk.

The breakfast cereal you ate probably contained corn that was genetically modified to decrease the use of pesticides and increase yields. If you had a piece of toast instead, that bread was made with yeast that helped it rise and stay fresh. If you ate cheese, it was likely made with an enzyme, chymosin, that biotech created more than 30 years ago. In the past, the chymosin (also known as rennin) was extracted from the stomachs of young calves. The use of yeast and chymosin can be traced back to the dawn of civilization.

When you get into your car, with your feet touching the carpet, you may have encountered another product of biotechnology. In many cars, the carpet was made using sustainable plant materials that reduce greenhouse gas emissions and require less energy.

Biotechnology already touches every part of your life.

In the United States, the bioeconomy makes up nearly three percent of the total Gross Domestic Product, some US$350 billion. The bioeconomy includes crops, drugs, fuels, industrial products and materials. The sector contributes more to the G.D.P. than mining and utilities, and almost as much as construction. In Canada, the bioeconomy, including farming, fishing, forestry and food, totaled some US$102 billion, more than motor vehicles and parts (US$87 billion), energy products (US$84 billion), and aircraft and parts (US$25 billion).

In 2006-2007, the monetary value of industrial and agricultural applications of biotech surpassed that of healthcare applications in the United States.[1]

Over the past decade from 2006 to 2016, the biotech sector is estimated to have grown on average nearly 15 percent per year—much faster than the rest of the economy.[2]

BIOLOGY IS PROGRAMMABLE

In the book that follows, we present three key concepts to help you appreciate the power of being able to program biology, how synthetic biology is having an impact on business, and why you need to pay attention and start incorporating biology into your business. We interview the innovators that are making the engineering of biology easier, and more accessible. They are creating tools and technologies, defining the practice of bio-fabrication, are using gene editing to disrupt existing industries, and are, at the same time, creating new industries.

But let's step back.

By biology, we mean all living matter on this planet. Life, as we know it.

By programmable, we are referring to the idea that you can digitize the common code that powers life—deoxyribonucleic acid, DNA. The DNA at the core of every organism can be read and written digitally. It can be engineered to modify organisms to produce new products. It can be engineered to create novel materials based on existing materials but with novel performance characteristics. It can be engineered to deliver drugs, increase health, remediate and save the environment. As you'll read in the following chapters, it's one of the most important resources that we have available to us.

What's Your Bio Strategy? grew out of conversations we had individually and together with academics, entrepreneurs, and investors.

It grew out of remembering the days just a few years ago when people would ask, "What's your digital strategy?" A question that evolved into, "What's your artificial intelligence strategy?" "What's your robotics strategy?" and, "What's your self-driving car strategy?"

It grew out of our experiences in the world of biotechnology and watching a new influx of academics and creatives arrive looking to innovate with the most fundamental building block on the planet.

It grew out of a group of academics and entrepreneurs defining a new field of biotechnology called synthetic biology whose primary goal was to make biology easier to engineer.

What's Your Bio Strategy? is a collection of interviews with several very wise people who have taught us, and are defining and redefining an industry. We've gotten to know most of them through SynBioBeta, the activity hub for synthetic biology that John founded in 2012, and through the work that Karl has done at messagingLAB since 2013.

Our hope is that you'll take the practical knowledge you gain from this book and look for ways to apply it to your business.

BIOLOGY OPERATES AT THE NANO- AND MEGA- SCALES

Somewhere near where you're reading this, grass is growing from a crack in a sidewalk, in the pavement.

No one knows how it got there.

It seemingly appeared from nowhere.

It grew on its own.

The seeds traveled an unknown distance, blown by the wind or dropped by a bird or rodent.

By chance, those seeds landed on soil.

They received water, sprouted roots, harvested nutrients from the soil, and pushed forth a shoot that oriented itself and reached toward the sun.

From the sun, it absorbed specific wavelengths of light and converted it into chemical energy in the form of carbohydrates. It also released oxygen into the atmosphere.

The blade of grass will continue to grow until it is time to produce more seeds that contain the same set of instructions to grow and produce more seeds, ad infinitum.

This activity is so random that it almost seems impossible that it would happen. Yet, no matter where you're reading this, you'll find those blades of grass growing from cracks in the sidewalk.

It's a miracle.

And it happens all over the world.

Life has had nearly 4 billion years of research and development to adapt to and shape our planet's diverse environments, and take advantage of diverse energy flows.

In their 1995 book *What is Life?* Lynn Margulis and Dorion Sanger wrote "Life on earth is more like a verb. It repairs, maintains, recreates, and outdoes itself."

Your body, we have come to learn, contains trillions of microorganisms. It's been estimated they outnumber human cells by ten to one. Yet because of their small size, they only make up one to three percent of your body mass. But they play a vital role in your health, something we are beginning to understand.

Biology operates on the invisible nanoscale, the microorganisms that live in and on our bodies, and on the megascale, the size of the

California Redwoods and the 2.4 square mile-sized honey fungus of the Blue Mountains of Oregon.

Our planet is the result of biology engineering itself through evolution, usually working slowly, sometimes working quickly, adapting to the environment, trying things out, and passing information promiscuously.

HUMANS HAVE A LONG HISTORY WITH BIOTECHNOLOGY, PART 1

Fermentation is the most basic form of using biology as a tool. We've been fermenting foods since the Neolithic or New Stone Age, some 10,000 years ago. The Neolithic is characterized by the first domesticated animals, basic agriculture, human settlements, and stone tools.

The Neolithic is also characterized by beer, wine, leavened bread, cheeses, yogurt, and pickles—fermented foods that nearly every global civilization counts in its culinary heritage.

Fermentation was probably discovered by accident. Our ancestors added salt to preserve food and that salt may have carried harmless microorganisms that caused it to ferment.[3] Fermentation changed the taste, made the food more digestible, increased its storage life, and made it more nutritious.

Scientifically, the microorganisms that ferment food—molds, yeasts, and bacteria—use enzymes, nature's power tools, to break nutrients (typically carbohydrates) into simpler compounds, such as alcohols and acids.[4]

Changes to food through fermentation can be sudden and dramatic. To our ancestors, those transformations must have been both mystery and miracle. The Egyptians praised Osiris the god of the dead and the underworld, for the brewing of beer. The Greeks established Bacchus as the god of wine. In Japan, a small shrine was central to all miso and shoyu breweries and was bowed to daily.

Today, every brewery depends on fermentation to create a valuable product from less valuable products. The basic ingredients of beer are cereal grains (the food source), hops (the flavoring), and yeast (the enzyme power tool that makes magic happen).

Today, nearly everyone in the United States lives within 10 miles of a microbrewery.

There's been a growing interest in fermented foods—plain yogurt, kimchi, kombucha, sauerkraut, and aged cheeses—because of the probiotics they contain and their positive interaction with our own gut microbiomes.

HUMANS HAVE A LONG HISTORY WITH BIOTECHNOLOGY, PART 2

Think of a dog. Any breed.

Border Collie. Chihuahua. German Shepherd. Great Dane. Greyhound. Poodle. Pug. Saint Bernard.

They all originate from a common wolf ancestor and were domesticated some 15,000 years ago. Dogs were the first domesticated animal. The variety of dogs rose from selective breeding.

The same is true of most domesticated animals—camels, canaries, cats, cattle, chickens, cows, ducks, geese, goats, goldfish, guinea pigs, horses, llamas, mice, laboratory rats, pigeons, sheep, rabbits, silk moths, turkeys, western honey bees, and yaks.

It is also true of most of the foods we eat. Grains such as wheat and rice have obvious relatives, but the grass known as teosinte looks nothing like today's modern corn.

Ancient farmers in what is known today as Mexico, started domesticating maize some 10,000 years ago.

It is believed these farmers noticed some plants grew larger than others. Maybe some kernels tasted better or were easier to grind. The farmers saved the kernels from plants with desirable characteristics and planted them for next season's harvest. Maize cobs became larger over time adding more rows of kernels, eventually taking on the form of the corn that we grow today.

This process, known as selective breeding or artificial selection, is biotechnology at its most basic.

WHY YOU NEED A BIO STRATEGY

"Uber yourself before you get Kodak'd."
—Dr. Daniel Kraft, xMed

Kodak held a dominant position in photographic film during much of the 20th Century. The company's well known tagline "Kodak moment" came to describe every important, personal event that was worth saving and savoring. Every event that demanded recording and memorializing.

These days, a Kodak moment is a warning to executives: Pay attention to disruptive developments, especially when they start to encroach on your market.

Until the mid-1970s, Kodak commanded 90 percent of the U.S. market for photographic film. With a market capitalization approaching some US$30 billion, it was one of the most powerful companies in the world.

Yet in 2012, the company filed for bankruptcy protection and exited the legacy film, photo developing, and scanners businesses that made it famous. It sold off its patents.

In 2013, Kodak re-emerged from bankruptcy as a much smaller technology company focused on imaging. Today, the company has a market capitalization of less than US$1 billion.

In contrast, Instagram, the mobile photo-sharing app, was started by two software entrepreneurs in 2010 and quickly registered more than 1 million users.

Two years later, it was acquired by Facebook for approximately US$1 billion in cash and stock—an amount that seemed excessive at the time.

Today, the app counts some 700 million users and is considered one of Facebook's major drivers of growth. In 2016, Forbes estimated that on its own Instagram would be worth between US$25 and US$50 billion.

In the interviews that follow, Amyris CEO John Melo noted that one of the reactions he gets from businesses that do not use biotechnology in their manufacturing is, "It sounds like a science experiment."

In our own conversations with non-biotech business people, we hear similar objections. Even those who are familiar with the concept of exponential technologies say, "Synthetic biology is still five to eight years away from making an impact."

When we explain how synthetic biology is already making an impact on major industries, the conversation changes. Executives want to understand how they can benefit from biotechnology today.

Kodak has come to exemplify missed opportunities. In the July 2016 issue of Harvard Business Review, Scott Anthony wrote, "[Kodak] is a sad story of lost potential. The American icon had the talent, the money, and even the foresight to make the transition. Instead, it ended up the victim of the aftershocks of a disruptive change."[5]

SYNTHETIC BIOLOGY MAKES BIOTECHNOLOGY ACCESSIBLE

At the start of 2017, the biotechnology industry is almost 50 years old. The industry enables fewer people to create value faster than individuals in established industries, such as construction, finance, mining, and transportation/logistics.

New technologies for working with biology, known collectively as *synthetic biology*, are evolving so quickly that there are multiple definitions for the field. Among them, *SyntheticBiology.org* and the *UK Royal Society* are:

> Synthetic biology is (a) the design and construction of new biological parts, devices, and systems, and (b) the re-design of existing natural biological systems for useful purposes.[6]

> Synthetic biology is an emerging area of research that can broadly be described as the design and construction of novel artificial biological pathways, organisms or devices, or the redesign of existing natural biological systems.[7]

The definitions are useful because they emphasize design and construction. They emphasize the redesign of existing biological systems because nature has given us a toolset.

In many ways, biotechnology today as practiced is an artisanal skill. The existing biotech tool set—the one biotechnology has used for the first 50 years of its history—is not adequate for the design and construction of new, predictable, and reproducible systems for useful purposes.

What's Your Bio Strategy? is a book about synthetic biology.

We simply define synthetic biology as a movement to "make biology easier to engineer."

Synthetic biology can be likened to the Web 2.0 movement that swept through Silicon Valley in the mid-2000s. Web 2.0 marked the rebirth of the internet after the Dotcom crash of 2001. It was characterized by a move from static web page to user-generated content, convergence, participation, social media, standardization, and usability (that is, ease of use by non-programmers). Companies birthed by Web 2.0 include Facebook, LinkedIn, Twitter and YouTube.

Similarly, synthetic biology is a rebirth of the biotechnology industry focused not necessarily on what is being made by biology, but the way it is being made. Synthetic biologists are changing the paradigm of biotechnology by applying the principles of engineering to biological systems. In 2001, Stanford professor Drew Endy codified the applications of computer science engineering principles such as abstraction, standardization, and specialization to biology.

For the past 50 years, microprocessors and information technology have disrupted and continue to disrupt most industries. The first commercial silicon chip microprocessor was introduced in 1971. According to Carlotta Perez' *Technological Revolutions and Financial Capital: The Dynamics of Bubbles and Golden Ages*, "Though practically no one realized it at the time, this was the big bang of a new universe of all-pervasive computing and digital communications."

The chips were powerful and cheap. They opened innumerable technological and undefined possibilities. They would transform the way people lived and worked around the world. When the internet appeared in 1994, the effect became exponential.

Though all life on Earth operates on a common code (DNA) and a central dogma (DNA encodes RNA, RNA encodes proteins), in some ways, biotechnologists have been hamstrung because there is no common set of tools. There is no application program interface (API) that makes it easy for disparate systems to communicate. There is no reproducible design capability. Standardization, for the most part is non-existent. Measuring the impact of cellular-level changes is a challenge.

The biology that enabled life on planet Earth is not a new technology. As Rob Carlson wrote in the opening to *Biology is Technology*, "Biology is the oldest technology." We are amateurs in engineering biology but we're good enough to disrupt markets and create new industries.

In contrast, metallurgy dates back some 7,000 years. It took more than 80 years to go from the Wright Brothers' flight at Kitty Hawk to the first commercial aircraft designed entirely using computer-aided design—Boeing's 777. In addition, the infrastructure for engineering biology is minuscule compared to, say, the oil industry.

While we use the analogy of the computer and the impact that it has had on society for the last 50 years, the analogy breaks down when you try to compare computers, which were designed by man to perform very specific functions, to living systems that, by their very nature, are designed to evolve.

It is not clear which analogy will dominate for synthetic biology. What is clear is that in just ten years, the advances that make it easier, faster, and cheaper to read and write DNA—the instructions of life— parallel discoveries making biology easier to engineer.

Biotechnology already impacts nearly every aspect of our lives, from the sheets we sleep on to the clothes we wear, the foods we eat, the ways we travel, the places we live, and the environment that surrounds us.

Synthetic biology is making biology easier to engineer. It is making the tools of biotechnology more accessible. It will enable and facilitate travel and sustainable life beyond earth. It is an economic engine with limitless potential.

In this book, we describe the advances that are making biotechnology accessible and easy to engineer. We interview the pioneers that started the field and the bio-entrepreneurs that are disrupting established industries. The interviews cover how synthetic biology is already displacing existing manufacturing methods, how the field is rapidly advancing and why companies need to have a strategy for incorporating biology into their businesses. We follow those interviews with a framework for incorporating synthetic biology into your business.

The people we interviewed are, for the most part, based in the United States. Yet the field is rapidly advancing in Europe and China. It is our intent to add more international voices in future editions.

SECTION 1. BIOLOGY IS PROGRAMMABLE AND ENGINEERABLE

"THREE PERCENT OF THE U.S. Gross Domestic Product. Domestic revenues growth at approximately 15 percent annually. People creating value faster than in established industries."

According to Bioeconomy Capital's Rob Carlson, biotechnology contributes some US$350 billion to the U.S. G.D.P. It contributes more than agriculture ($247B) and mining ($290B), but less than construction ($530B) and arts and entertainment ($591B). In contrast, the 2012 revenues for the global semiconductor industry totaled some $322 billion.

While U.S. domestic growth has averaged 2.4 percent since the 1960s, the biotechnology industry's 15 percent growth is impressive by any standard, especially when you consider that it takes fewer people to create significant value. A pair of bio-engineers with a laptop and access to a lab can create a molecule that is worth billions of dollars.

Since the discovery of DNA's twisted-ladder structure by Rosalind Franklin, James Watson, and Francis Crick in the 1950s, and the founding of Genentech, the first biotechnology company by Robert Swanson and Herbert Boyer in 1976, the applications of engineering biology have multiplied.

As an industry, biotechnology is almost 50 years old. All around us, biotech touches and improves all aspects of our lives by increasing agricultural yields and protecting crops, creating better, more precise medicines, and providing natural solutions to industrial problems.

Yet, most people have no idea that biotechnology touches their lives every day.

In this section, we have interviewed the synthetic biology pioneers who are making biology easier to engineer and driving the field forward scientifically. You'll read about current and future challenges, as well as the tremendous impact creativity and new entrants are having on the field.

DARLENE SOLOMON: BIOTECH ALREADY TOUCHES YOUR LIFE EVERY DAY

DARLENE SOLOMON, Ph.D., serves as the senior vice president and chief technology officer for Agilent Technologies. Agilent is a company founded on the technology and ability to measure the world around us. Darlene leads Agilent Labs with a focus on life sciences and diagnostics, and manages the company's university relations, corporate library, and external venture investments. In her leadership role, she works closely with Agilent's businesses to define the company's technology strategy and research and development priorities.

JOHN CUMBERS: How do people interact with biotechnology on a daily basis?

DARLENE SOLOMON: Most people don't realize they touch and benefit from bio-based or biologically-manufactured products every day. Textiles and plastic containers, the contact lens solution, and medicines are often either partially or entirely biologically-based or manufactured using biological production methods. Since it's not on the label—and doesn't have to be—it looks like the same product they've always purchased. Only it's now made with biotech.

KARL SCHMIEDER: The modern biotechnology industry is about 40 years old, how do you think it's progressed?

DARLENE SOLOMON: In many ways, I think the expectation has been higher than the outcomes. Don't get me wrong, I don't want to discount the successes we've seen with therapeutics and the early days of precision medicine. In some areas, like cancer, biotech has made it easier to diagnose and understand diseases with unprecedented resolution. The challenge is that biology is much more complex than other disciplines.

For example, some people expected the Human Genome Project—the effort to sequence all three billion base pairs that make up our DNA and identify within this code more than 20,000 human genes—would solve human health problems.

Fifteen years later, we're just capturing the benefits of that international project. That work laid the foundation for technologies like cellular reprogramming, stem-cell technologies, regenerative medicine, and cellular manufacturing. We're now positioned for disruptive, accelerating change, and biotech will impact even more people every day.

JOHN CUMBERS: You say biology is more complex than other disciplines—how does it compare to engineering disciplines?

DARLENE SOLOMON: Engineering disciplines and the physical sciences, while very sophisticated, are well understood, deeply modeled and ultimately predictable. This is not the case for biology today.

We've been studying physics for centuries. Even engineering has a 4,000-year-old history. Biology as an engineering discipline is very new and more complex. We still have decades to go.

For example, I like to contrast the difference between transistors and cells. Transistors are well-behaved when they're part of a circuit board. What they do is predictable. It can be measured and it can be engineered.

Biology, on the other hand, is always growing and evolving. If you have two discrete cells with the same DNA, they will act differently depending on their environment. You don't yet have [complete] wiring diagrams with cells. You don't have oscillators or signal analyzers to measure what is happening on the whole cellular level.

KARL SCHMIEDER: Yet biotechnology has been very successful and contributes significantly to the global GDP. How do you account for that?

DARLENE SOLOMON: Compared to traditional manufacturing, biological manufacturing can be more profitable. Many large chemical companies understand the potential of biology, though their efforts might still be relatively limited. In many cases they still need to overcome the perceived risk of these investments and ensure economic viability in the early stages.

Bio-manufacturing opens up new opportunities to create things that weren't previously possible. You can create novel materials that provide superior performance, while at the same time being sustainable and potentially more profitable. Companies that have been successful with biology can leverage their learnings and start thinking about how to take their knowledge to the next adjacent opportunity.

Europe has passed some meaningful legislation around new sustainability targets that I think will further drive bio-based manufacturing. Many companies will need to meet those mandates by 2020 which is in just a few years away.

JOHN CUMBERS: What should non-biotech companies know about biotechnology?

DARLENE SOLOMON: The challenges and opportunities of biology are driving major transformations. Companies need to be ready. Biotechnology is going to have a disruptive impact on the petroleum economy. Biology will challenge our policies and regulatory systems. In some ways, non-biotech folks may not see those impacts before being impacted directly.

In the near-term, we're probably going to see a lot more progress on the health care and medicinal side of biotechnology. I mentioned cancer as a disease whose diagnosis and treatment has changed tremendously because of biotechnology. But when you look at biologically-based therapeutics, we're still in the early phases.

We're also going to see a renaissance in natural products therapeutics and the Westernization of traditional Chinese medicines. Those products and medicines will be rigorously characterized. We'll gain a much better understanding of what makes them work. Since both natural products and Chinese medicines consist of interesting active molecules, they are more amenable to being manufactured biologically. This could result in traditional Chinese medicines becoming more widely used.

In another 20 or 30 years, living matter will become a pervasive and standard tool. There will be many more skills and methods. As a result, more objectives will be achieved. It's going to touch everything around us and improve the quality of life for both humanity and our planet.

The vision among many of us in the field is that we'll be able to take the engineering cycle of design-test-build, and apply it to cells and organisms. We'll be able to model and predict biology the same way we are able to do with more mature engineering disciplines. We'll better understand cellular complexity and be able to profile all the biochemistry in a single cell, group of cells, or organisms. As we're able to understand that, we'll be able to probe and model the interactions between cells. Overall, we have very exciting times ahead.

J. CRAIG VENTER: UNDERSTANDING BIOLOGY ALLOWS US TO IMPROVE HUMANITY

J. CRAIG VENTER, PH.D., HAS been a pioneer in genomic research since the 1990s when he and his team developed a new technique to rapidly discover genes. In 1995, Dr. Venter and his colleagues sequenced the first free-living organism, *Haemophilus influenza*. In 1998, he made history when he and his for-profit company, Celera, challenged the U.S. government's Human Genome Project to a DNA-sequencing race. Now, Dr. Venter runs J. Craig Venter Institute, a nonprofit, and two biotech firms, Human Longevity and Synthetic Genomics (SGI). He is the author of *A Life Decoded: My Genome, My Life* and *Life at the Speed of Light: From the Double Helix to the Dawn of Digital Life.*

JOHN CUMBERS: Could you give us a vision for the next 20 years of synthetic biology?

CRAIG VENTER: If we're going to control biology, let's truly control it to change the outcome of humanity. For example, it would be interesting to design a set of synthetic bacteria or a bacterial strain that could secrete known molecules to turn on groups of stem cells or turn off senescent cells.[8] Stem cells become quiescent over time. If we knew how to turn them on with molecular sensors or killer T-cells,[9] then we could live 300 years.

JOHN CUMBERS: Are you suggesting you engineer your own cells? Or would these be engineered cells that would be added to your body?

CRAIG VENTER: I think we could engineer generic cells that would work on anyone.

KARL SCHMIEDER: If that's the vision for synthetic biology in 20 years, what stands in the way?

CRAIG VENTER: Lack of money or a field for doing this. Nobody wants to fund long-term projects. You can't get funding for 20-year projects, not that we intend to work on projects that long. If we had 30 labs around the world trying to design different cell types we would make tremendous progress.

JOHN CUMBERS: Nearly 20 years ago, you started working on a synthetic cell that would contain the smallest genome of any known, independent organism. Did you go through the standard engineering cycle to make that work?

CRAIG VENTER: Yes. Our vision for the minimal cell was to build a compiler.[10] We went through the design-build-test cycle. We started with designs and took those as far as we could. Then, we built and tested. It's what happened with the airline industry, over a different timescale.

KARL SCHMIEDER: How do we make the jump from designing a minimal cell to your vision that we live 300 years?

CRAIG VENTER: In the past, I've quoted Felix Le Dantec, a 19th century biologist and philosopher who said, "Give me a living protoplasm and I will re-make the whole animal and vegetable kingdoms." At that time, they didn't know what proteins were so they called it a protoplasm. The minimal cell is a minimal protoplasm.

In theory, we should be able to program the minimal cell genetically to convert it to a cell with a cell wall. We can convert it into an archaea, a prokaryote, or maybe a photosynthetic cell. That's additive evolution.

We had talked about running a contest to see who could take the minimal cell and rapidly evolve it into something else. There could be an annual prize for the person or team that took the biggest evolutionary step forward. A contest like that could attract a highly motivated group of people that would advance synthetic genomics by orders of magnitude. Other than Defense Advanced Research Projects Agency

(DARPA), no one else has done this. We've self-funded this work for 20 years.

The question remains, is this not interesting enough to do? Is the hurdle too high? There should be 50 projects like this right now. Groups should be trying to improve what we have done and take things further. I don't think any of this should be too hard to do. Some of it is basic science. Some projects could produce drugs like insulin rapidly and inexpensively.

JOHN CUMBERS: It's been predicted that biotechnology will have an enormous impact on consumer goods, do you agree?

CRAIG VENTER: It could be a big opportunity. I believe strongly in using science for the betterment of humanity. We should be striving for that first and foremost, whether it's creating new kinds and sources of food, developing new energy sources, or creating a sustainable economy.

The big issues facing humanity can be solved with biology. We need to feed 9 to 10 billion people, provide energy, and clean, potable water. We're currently destroying our environment at an increasing pace. Biology stands to become the number one sustainable energy source in history.

At SGI, we've designed a nutritionally perfect protein from algae. It didn't require much synthetic biology. The people working on it designed perfectly nutritious proteins with better flavorings. Companies like General Mills can take our algae-based protein, use their extrusion technologies and create textures like meat or chicken.

If we jump ahead 50 to 100 years, I see very little farming because agriculture is fundamentally anti-nature. I see biological factories producing foods. It's more efficient and better for the environment.

SGI has worked with Exxon-Mobil to double the production of algal cells and produce bio-fuels. Unfortunately, interest in bio-fuels is fad driven. There is interest and funding, then interest dies. Exxon is taking a longer view. They know they will run out of oil and they know they'll need alternative fuel sources.

If you take a natural gas-fired power plant, collect the exhaust, and you run it through algae, you can capture a significant amount of the CO_2. You can take that algae, harvest it, and burn it as fuel. Right now, this isn't that efficient because we still have low-cost natural gas and fuels. But if governments were to impose a real carbon tax, it would eliminate coal, no matter how cheap it is. We could tax coal out of existence so that people would be forced to advance and use cleaner energy sources.

Water is one of the biggest problems in the world. Biological systems could be engineered into natural filters and solve that problem.

The Sorcerer expedition[11] has been collecting plastic at sea. Instead of using a fishing net, we are using a "plankton" net because ocean plastic is being broken down until it's invisible. At that stage of decomposition, it's much more harmful to the marine environment. Creating or selecting microbes that eat the plastic might take some thoughtful genetic engineering.

Synthetic biology can deliver significant contributions to solve the issues that humanity faces. People want to fund groups to advance things faster. We need that funding to create a synthetic biology economy because it will provide successful solutions to the world's biggest challenges. That's where I'd like to see things go. The potential is there.

I started Synthetic Genomics as a virtual company to fund the Institute to make the synthetic cell and prove it was possible. But Synthetic Genomics was forced to become a real company, because so many people were interested in solving real problems. To create the solutions to humanity's challenges and advance the field of synthetic biology, this needs to happen at 1000 times the scale.

JOHN CUMBERS: The cost of getting a new plant in the field is $200 million. What needs to happen to the regulatory environment to accelerate the release of more genetically modified systems?

CRAIG VENTER: I'm advocating the opposite. I'm advocating for closed systems.

Over the years, agriculture has gotten substantially more efficient but farming, as previously mentioned, is fundamentally anti-nature. It's a two-dimensional manufacturing system that requires millions of acres and massive amounts of water that doesn't even get used in biological production.

Instead of releasing novel traits into the environment, let's create closed systems. Let's avoid the possibility of gene hopping from one system to another.

Biologic manufacturing systems can take up one-ten thousandth of the space that farming requires. That gives nature a lot of space to come back and replenish the natural cycles of the planet.

I'm also advocating that we change the definition of food. The flavor world can provide flavors. The texture world can provide textures. Microbes, algae, and other manufactured and nutritious foods can be created in sterile, clean conditions. We have to go in that direction for efficiency and food safety.

KARL SCHMIEDER: Are there any businesses that you believe won't be impacted by biotechnology?

CRAIG VENTER: Maybe the steel industry? It's much easier to come up with industries that will be impacted. For example, we're working with United Therapeutics to redesign the pig genome. We're using a combination of tools to insert landing pads in the chromosomes so that we can easily insert new genes. We've been using CRISPR to edit the genes.[12]

The thing holding us back is the cost of gene synthesis. If DNA synthesis cost 1/100th of a penny per base pair, we would have synthesized every possible combination necessary to get a life form. We could build 3000 versions and test for the one that worked the best, instead of engineering one gene at a time.

When the price of DNA synthesis falls there will be a revolution in synthetic genomics and synthetic biology. The commercial market isn't big enough to push the technology and the government isn't driving that.

I'm optimistic about synthetic biology. I'm just not optimistic about the timeframe it might take for this to turn into a real field.

How much does DNA synthesis cost per base pair?

PAM SILVER: WE MUST APPROACH SYNTHETIC BIOLOGY SYSTEMATICALLY

IN 2004, PAM SILVER PH.D., became one of the founding members of the Department of Systems Biology at Harvard Medical School and the first Director of the Harvard University Ph.D. Program in Systems Biology. In 2009, she became one of the first members of the Harvard University Wyss Institute for Biologically Inspired Engineering. Last year, Pam made news for the co-creation of a bionic leaf that combined synthetic biology and chemistry to make fuel from sunlight, water, and air.

JOHN CUMBERS: You've been on a mission to make biology easier to engineer—how do you think the field is doing?

PAM SILVER: Fair to medium. Part of the problem is that people lose sight of that mission. People can engineer things with biology. They make things that get published, but there needs to be more value creation. At least in academia. The point is to engineer biology faster, cheaper, and more predictably, in a way where the information can be useful to the community at large.

KARL SCHMIEDER: If that's the case, what constitutes success? Could you give us an example?

PAM SILVER: One of my overarching goals has been biological computing with real-world applications. One application is sensing something, counting forward, and telling us when an event happens. That system involves a sensor, a counter, and an actuator. Those are all things that synthetic biology would like to and can do. We set out to do this a few years ago and most recently, succeeded in the gut microbiome. For me, this was a personal milestone as it combined engineered genetic circuits with a real world application.

The broader question of what defines success has many answers. For example, yeast that produce opiates is a real game changer. Rapid engineering of organisms that produce never-before-seen chemicals and materials would be a huge success. Students of synthetic biology should think about success as beyond the next publishable result.

JOHN CUMBERS: Do you think things like standardized parts are making biology easier to engineer?

PAM SILVER: The concept of parts in engineering biology has had a huge impact. From our own work for example, we discovered peptides that target proteins to the nucleus. These are highly modular and can be attached to virtually any protein and change its location in the cell.

Synthetic biology has focused a great deal on gene circuit design where similar modularity of parts such as promoters and ribosome binding sites are key. Registries of biological parts have grown and been deployed by for example the International Genetically Engineered Machine (iGEM) competition teams over the years.[13] The extent to which these parts have been standardized begs the question of what standardization really means. If we are going to have standards, then efforts to generate a set of standards are still needed.

We are still in the early days of being able to reliably engineer a complex genetic circuit from parts. However, as we move from parts assembly to DNA synthesis as the strategy for circuit design—the pace towards achieving this goal should increase.

JOHN CUMBERS: Do you think the next framework for engineering biology will come from academia or industry? Do you think we need a Bell Labs or Xerox Parc to create new paradigms for engineering biology?

PAM SILVER: I'm not interested in developing frameworks. I want to solve problems. A better way to approach this would be to have a common work environment where engineers can work together with biologists. People could develop foundational technologies when they're working to achieve goals. Where this occurs will depend on risk taking by institutions and/or government or foundations.

If there were one foundational technology holding people back, it's a source of DNA synthesis. DNA is the core substrate for engineering biology and it needs to be accessible to all rapidly and of high quality.

JOHN CUMBERS: Does academia prepare scientists adequately to go into industry as synthetic biologists?

PAM SILVER: Silicon Valley was started by academics, real visionaries who either started companies or pushed their students to start companies. For example, [Frederick] Terman, the father of Silicon Valley, pushed Dave Packard to start Hewlett Packard.

The academic enterprise is good because people need to learn biology and the basics of engineering. However, my understanding is that when someone comes out of academia and goes into industry, the company needs to start training them all over again. More synergy between academia and industry helps in this regard.

KARL SCHMIEDER: Do you think that deductive reasoning will be necessary as better computer programs are developed to facilitate the engineering of biology?

PAM SILVER: I'm pretty naive on this but there does seem to be a tipping point, when you go from an academic discipline to one that is solely industrial because of computation—take search for example.

With regard to synthetic biology, I've dabbled in metabolic engineering and always found it to be extremely difficult. If someone came to me with a metabolic engineering project, my response might be, "Can we outsource that to Ginkgo BioWorks?" However, I think it's still useful to keep biological knowledge in the mix, at least for now.

For example, a few years ago, we created a counter that would report whether or not mice had been exposed to antibiotics. It measured and counted antibiotic response. We published the paper and people would ask "How many versions did you have to build to get that to work?" I would answer, "Five." We didn't set up a high-throughput screen to build that circuit. We knew the biology necessary to make it work. The ideology that you can create any possible circuit without knowing any biology still seems a ways off but moving faster all the time.

KARL SCHMIEDER: People compare synthetic biology to computer science, is that an apt comparison?

PAM SILVER: The computer industry is driven by faster, cheaper, smaller. That was the main driver of Moore's Law. Is there an equivalent in synthetic biology? Some have called biology the best nanotechnology. Biology operates on different time scales. There are some aspects that are as fast as an electronic circuit. Biology is already small. It works on the level of chemical bonds. The engineering of biology should be cheap, but it's not yet.

JOHN CUMBERS: What do you think non-scientists need to understand about synthetic biology?

PAM SILVER: They should know what defines success. If you're going to make a commodity, whether it's high-value or low-value, you need to know how fast you can hit your profit margin. Often times the question is can biology compete with chemistry. You have to find the things that fit the ideal for making a profit. It often colors the view of synthetic biology and what's possible with biology.

KARL SCHMIEDER: Does that take into account the cost of the petroleum necessary to create that product? Or, the fact that they could gain a competitive advantage by manufacturing with biology?

PAM SILVER: Large commodity companies where synthetic biology has promise have to calculate when they're losing money. I've heard it said that if the molecule is six carbons or less, they're going to rely on chemistry. For anything bigger or more complex, they might consider using biology. Large companies need to understand how biology will impact their business, whether short-term or long-term.

JOHN CUMBERS: What are some strategies that you think industry could adopt to encourage more women to start companies?

PAM SILVER: The issue around women starting companies is not unique to synthetic biology. Some women start out thinking they would like to start companies but it gets beaten out of them pretty quickly because of the male dominance of the field. It is well documented that the VC community is primarily male and the resulting startups are often lead by males. I have had discussions with some local VCs about these issues but have not seen a lot of progress.

However, now that it is more out in the open, we can at least have a discussion and see where things go.

KARL SCHMIEDER: What can industry do to change that?

PAM SILVER: If you don't take aggressive prescriptive behavior nothing will change. It can start with the speakers at meetings. If you hold a meeting and you don't have women speakers, you're going to hear from me and others. I think that is helping. To be honest, I do think things are getting better. However, if you are in VC and you think males are going to make a better impression on mostly male investors, how are you going to change that? The progress is small but it is happening. It seems like things are changing. But the only way to change is to empower everyone who wants to see a future for synthetic biology.

PIERRE MONSAN: UNDERSTANDING LIVING SYSTEMS IS MORE IMPORTANT THAN MARS

PIERRE MONSAN, Ph.D., is a Toulouse-based serial entrepreneur and Founding Director of the Toulouse White Biotechnology incubator. A renowned expert in biocatalysis and biological systems engineering processes, Dr. Monsan serves as professor emeritus at the National Institute for Applied Sciences (INSA) of the University of Toulouse and Professor at Mines ParisTech (Department of Biotechnology).

KARL SCHMIEDER: You've been involved in biotechnology for 40 years. What are the biggest changes you've seen?

PIERRE MONSAN: In the 1970s, we were focused on isolating enzymes. In the 1980s, we witnessed the molecular biology and biotechnology revolutions. In the 1990s, it was extremophiles and high-throughput screening, enzyme and cell design. Now, we're in the midst of the synthetic biology revolution. Truthfully, there is no revolution, there is only evolution.

The growth of scientific knowledge is breathtaking. What we were doing in the 1970s and 1980s with random, chemical or radiation mutagenesis was totally uncontrolled. It allowed us to obtain stable and efficient enzymes, which were useful to obtain microorganisms good at producing amino acids, organic acids, and vitamins. Those bugs were the basis of an industry that most people don't even know exists. It appears that it would have been very difficult to obtain those mutations rationally. Now, we can create such mutations rationally, by design, but will we reach the same efficiency than when using random approaches?

It raises a scientific question—is it really possible to use rational design to create something that does what we want it to? Living systems don't like to be forced. When you metabolically engineer a microorganism, you're often surprised as to how quickly the bug will reorganize its genome. That's nature and that's what it does.

We need more tools to design genomes. The gene editing tools zinc fingers and Talens were expensive and time-consuming to use. Now you can use [the gene editing tools] CRISPR-CAS9 for US$30. Who would have imagined that?

KARL SCHMIEDER: France has always been a technology leader in biotechnology. How do you think you're doing in terms of synthetic biology?

PIERRE MONSAN: Basic research is progressing, but we need more of a business orientation. Our basic research is great. We've organized some great synthetic biology teams, but we need more technology transfers to industry.

Interestingly, Louis Pasteur started working on applied industrial and health problems, then he worked his way back to the basic science.

It's great to see younger scientists who are more business-oriented and have fewer inhibitions than older scientists. A young colleague was working as a biochemist and found a microorganism that produced a blue dye. He went straight to Hermes to show them. Now we're helping him and his company—Pili Biotech—figure out how to scale production.

Another company I'm working with, Glowee[14], is working to eliminate city lights by creating plants that use the luciferase enzymes from marine organisms. They're already working with NASA.

With synthetic biology, we dream to use cheap, available carbon sources to create valuable molecules. To do that, we need to better understand microorganisms and how they function. That will accelerate the breakthroughs.

I believe that over the next 20 years, our increase in knowledge will enable more applications. We'll continue to use biotechnology as a technology in existing markets like agriculture, chemistry, food,

and medicine, but I'm not sure we'll also create new markets. The internet is a new market. Mobile is a new market. That said, DNA for data storage will be a new market. The ability of a company like Twist Bioscience to expand the use of DNA for data storage will open new fields.

KARL SCHMIEDER: One of the rate limiting steps for synthetic biology is the ability to scale production. How can companies overcome that?

PIERRE MONSAN: It requires two things. First, you need a very stable, very robust [microbial] strain that will work at scale. Second, you need to understand that the people who work in a lab are very different from those that work in a production plant. The levels of education are different, so you need to tailor your methodologies for them.

KARL SCHMIEDER: As biotechnology becomes more accessible through the tools of synthetic biology will the rate-limiting steps change?

PIERRE MONSAN: There's no easy answer. Synthetic biology is a fantastic tool to increase our knowledge of the way microorganisms function, specifically, understanding metabolic pathways, their regulation and interconnections. Those pathways are complicated and interdependent. If one gets switched off, another gets turned on. Our understanding of those pathways will make it easier to control microbes.

We still don't have enough knowledge to take a rational design approach for new bugs. We use *E. coli* and yeast all the time but we still don't know exactly how they work.

KARL SCHMIEDER: Those are the preferred industrial tools.

PIERRE MONSAN: That's right. The challenge with new microorganisms is we don't have the genetic tools to do the modifications. For example, in France, the company Deinove works with *Deinococcus*, but when they started, they had to develop the genetic tools because nothing existed.

I like the pragmatic approach taken by Japanese scientists. They continue to do a lot of traditional, basic screening, while at the same time pushing the frontiers with molecular design. That's important.

You can't neglect either approach. You need both. You need microbiology because it gives you the feeling of touching a living system on an agar plate, the way you hold an animal in your hand. A microorganism is not just a piece of DNA that you cut and paste. Too many things happen beyond the level of DNA.

KARL SCHMIEDER: Building on that idea microorganisms as industrial tools, what tools would make your research easier?

PIERRE MONSAN: I'm an enzymologist so I want to understand whole cell functioning, not just single protein or enzyme function. I'd like to be able to look at the molecular dynamics of a protein.

The secret of life is it's always in motion. People think of protein structure as static because we look at crystals but in fact, biomolecules are always in motion. They're always interacting with each other. We can see some of that with nuclear magnetic resonance (NMR), but we don't see enough.

KARL SCHMIEDER: Do you think computer modeling, or perhaps augmented or virtual reality modeling will help with that? Especially given that we don't understand the number of processes and interactions happening at a subcellular level.

PIERRE MONSAN: Absolutely. I could imagine visualization tools evolving from computational modeling to virtual reality. It might not be real-time but it could be modeled that way. That would be extremely useful.   SDGR ?

In a cell, enzymes are operating everywhere. They're on the inside and outside of the cell membrane. We don't have enough information about these key interactions and the roles they play in living systems.

KARL SCHMIEDER: A U.S.-based synthetic biology and a bio-fabrication company have a designer on staff, how do you think that impacts biotechnology company?

PIERRE MONSAN: It's important because it opens minds and encourages creativity. My general feeling is that scientific research is less creative than it could be. There is so much pressure on evaluation. People don't have time, at least in France, to pursue blue sky research. At TWB, we invest about one million U.S. dollars per year in a very basic, very risky, blue sky projects to generate creativity and intellectual property.

We need more crazy ideas. We need to use synthetic biology to move beyond replacing the petroleum economy. We know chemistry will never produce polysaccharides or proteins, but the challenge is economics. We need to open markets. The only way to do that is through creativity.

KARL SCHMIEDER: Any final thoughts?

PIERRE MONSAN: We ought to invest more in understanding living systems than going to Mars. I understand the desire to leave our planet and take the human race into the solar system but understanding biology is more important. The guys in physics and space exploration are really good at raising money, biologists need to get just as good.

RODRIGO MARTINEZ: IS THE BIOECONOMY IRRELEVANT?

IN 1997, HARVARD PROFESSOR JUAN Enríquez and Rodrigo Martinez introduced the term 'bioeconomy' to describe the economic impact of biotechnology. Enriquez and Martinez examined the flow of genetic data into the world's three largest public genetic databases—the U.S. National Institutes of Health GenBank,[15] the European Molecular Biology Laboratory (EMBL)[16] and the DNA Database of Japan (DDBJ)[17]. They published their findings in *Science Magazine* and presented at the 1997 American Association for the Advancement of Science meeting.

JOHN CUMBERS: How has the concept of the bioeconomy changed over time?

what happened in 1977? Genentech?

RODRIGO MARTINEZ: In 1997, the modern biotechnology industry was barely twenty years old. We could see things happening in agriculture and healthcare. A few chemical companies were applying biology to their manufacturing processes. We saw signals that biotechnology was delivering economic activity in a company's business unit or a line of products. It was a very small segment when we looked at the total economy.

At the time, the economy was changing. The term digital economy had entered the mainstream. Everyone was talking about how digital would transform business. You had the dot com crash and eventually we reached a point where no one talked about digital business anymore. Compare the number of Google searches for digital economy starting in 1999 to today and the search term is irrelevant because all business is digital. Sure, there are probably people still creating economic value with Windows 95, but they're quickly losing to artificial intelligence.

When digital touched every segment of the economy—because everything is conducted with or connected through digital—we stopped talking about the digital economy. There was an inflection point when more than half of the Fortune 500 were using digital tools for their operations and productivity. The next inflection point happened when companies began existing only because digital enabled what they do. Think about Apple when it started offering iTunes in 2001 or so. A few years later, you have Facebook, Twitter and Amazon. Those four are an inflection point.

KARL SCHMIEDER: At what point would you say biology has impacted Fortune 500 companies?

RODRIGO MARTINEZ: Do you mean at what point do companies use biological tools that improve their operations and productivity? At what point do most of the Fortune 500 companies have some connection to biotechnologies in the broadest sense of the word?

I don't think we're there yet, but there are signs. Companies in the Fortune 500 are already using genetic algorithms.[15] Some are producing dyes using biotech. Some might be using biological tools. On the other hand, we're leapfrogging some of the steps that were needed to build the digital economy. Companies like Ginkgo BioWorks and Synthetic Genomics exist solely because the technology is available.

Today, even if less than one-tenth of Fortune 500 companies are using biotechnology, you see it spreading quickly. I've said this before, I think the term bioeconomy is becoming irrelevant. It might already be obsolete. It's just the economy. The biological part of the economy—biotechnology, synthetic biology, the use of biology to create things without biotech—is becoming interspersed with everything. The economy is biology and biology is the economy.

JOHN CUMBERS: How do you think cities and our everyday lives will change as biology becomes an integral part of our everyday lives?

RODRIGO MARTINEZ: I'm always asking myself, how do we create the mindsets that allow us to imagine the products and services that people will be using every day as a result of the different types of biotechnologies, biological technologies.

If I told you you're going to create fabrics from a biological source, you'd say OK. You can see that. Maybe Gap buys Ginkgo BioWorks and turns it into a materials manufacturer. Your house might be equipped with a device that prints your clothes while you're taking a shower. You put it on. It molds to your body and changes color. It keeps you fresh and clean all day long. And at night, you recycle it.

We could sit down with a couple of glasses of wine and come up with 50 ideas. Do either of you have a 3D printer at home?

JOHN CUMBERS: No.

KARL SCHMIEDER: No. We talked about it a few years ago.

RODRIGO MARTINEZ: Three to five years ago we all thought we'd have one. We don't because the question is, what do I do with it?

We will probably make custom clothing or clothing will be produced on demand using biomaterials. We're going to spin, grow, print things and will need a new language to describe what we do with these new biomaterials.

You might subscribe to designs and patterns from The Gap or Banana Republic and they'll get printed at home. If that happens, what will be the role of shopping malls or stores?

When I go through these thought exercises, I force myself to think, "How does this change your life? What are the implications for other industries? What opportunities and threats are created?"

There are already companies that you take a picture with your phone, send it to them, and a few days later it arrives beautifully framed, or printed on glass. I think we will see some really interesting ideas around art for your house using biology. Maybe it's a living bacterium that evolves and changes over time. We already know flavors, fragrances, and foods will change.

We are already having disagreements on what we should be able to change in ourselves. That is going to be an enormous debate in the next ten years. When we understand our own microbiome, we'll start creating products that interact with the trillions of bacteria that live in or on us. You'll start to make connections across industries.

The Gap patterns that I download and print every day could include information on my microbiome. A connected device in my kitchen could monitor the food I eat and suggest I eat pickles that I also make at home to keep my immune systems strong.

There are signals that all of this is happening. You don't need to understand the science behind it. You don't need to even know there is science. You just know apples or pickles are in your fridge because you need these foods to stay healthy.

JOHN CUMBERS: Do you think we need to have a Windows 95-type program that makes biology easier to engineer? Or a Netscape moment so that companies can visualize what is possible with engineered biology?

RODRIGO MARTINEZ: We're past the BASIC stage. We don't need to teach people how to program in BASIC before they can create with mycelium, learn to brew or create bio-fabrics. People shouldn't need to learn how to use UNIX before they can use a digital biology program.

I used to think you needed a set of tools to get people excited about biotech, but I'm getting away from that idea. It's a little bit like telling the world they need to learn computer aided design to start using computers.

To get people excited about biology, you need to start deploying resources—people, money and minds—to change companies. Companies need to forget the past, imagine the future, and define the steps to get there. Companies need to visualize what will be possible with biology in five, ten, 30 years and design ten different biology-based models right now.

That doesn't necessarily mean using synthetic biology. Learn from nature and leverage four billion years of research and development. That might be biotechnology for some companies, for others it might mean cellular pathways, or genetics, and for others it might mean mycelium.

Companies will get excited when we begin creating ten different business models, ten ways to improve the environment while increasing profits, ten ways to engage their customers, their employees, ten ways to communicate their applications of biology to their customers. None of those need to be mutually exclusive.

The power of triggering a conversation about biology is that there are thousands of companies that need exposure to the basic ideas. They need to imagine how it will transform the way they do things.

KARL SCHMIEDER: That requires a mindset shift and a willingness to imagine what could be possible.

RODRIGO MARTINEZ: Exactly. It's not about learning there's an incredible and powerful new computer code based on four letters that allows you to do things better. If you're going to start with Windows 95 and imagine moving to the Cloud, it's going to take 15 years. No one has 15 years.

Companies need to create an internal group of pirates who are tasked with thinking about what biology will enable tomorrow, next year, and in the future. They need to think about how biology will transform their business and how they start getting there today. Without that group, they'll be lost. It'll be Instagram, Amazon Shared Services and Uber all over again, only the impact of biology will be much greater.

PAUL FREEMONT: CREATIVITY IS DRIVING INNOVATION IN SYNTHETIC BIOLOGY

PAUL FREEMONT, PH.D., HEADS THE Section of Structural Biology in the Department of Medicine at Imperial College London. He is also co-founder of synthetic biology research at Imperial College which includes the National United Kingdom Innovation and Knowledge Centre for Synthetic Biology (SynbiCITE)[19] and the London DNA Foundry. A leading voice for synthetic biology in the United Kingdom, Dr. Freemont is also very active in engaging the public on synthetic biology.

JOHN CUMBERS: You were one of the authors of the United Kingdom's synthetic biology roadmap. Can you describe how synthetic biology fits into the U.K.'s innovation strategy?

PAUL FREEMONT: The U.K.'s innovation strategy is currently being reconsidered as part of the governments industrial strategy paper which was released earlier this year. At the moment synthetic biology is not explicitly stated in the strategy but through SynbiCITE, we are lobbying the government hard to include it.

SynbiCITEs primary objective is to accelerate and promote the commercialization of synthetic biology research and technology and since we started nearly 4 years ago we have been part of developing a fledgling ecosystem of startups and spinouts. In fact, we just published a report on the U.K. startup scene in synthetic biology so everyone can check out the community and companies and see for themselves the growth that is happening—it's exciting but somewhat behind the US.

At SynbiCITE, we're seeking to see "How could synthetic biology disrupt major industries or even develop new markets for biotechnology?"

As you know the U.K. has a very well established and world-leading creative industry and what's interesting is that synthetic biology is reaching into areas like fashion, architecture, art and design, and textiles as well as the traditional tech innovation which is blossoming in London at the moment. There's a real entrepreneurship culture shift in the U.K. the scale of which we have never seen before. It seems to be a generational thing. It's focused around major metropolitan areas like London and Cambridge and is fed by the great universities we have. To a small extent it mirrors what's happening in the [San Francisco] Bay Area or in Boston with innovation driving a very healthy startup culture which is not only university spin outs but a healthy proportion of non-traditional startups. This is beginning to impact on the small creative maker-type industries that are much more open to innovation and cool new things like synthetic biology.

For bigger companies and major industries, synthetic biology is still not penetrating as much as it should. Still, we need to see more examples of the technology making an impact so we can go to the chief technical officer at say a big traditional chemicals company and show them the amazing capabilities that engineered biology provides. Several large say more traditional bio-industries like Pharma already have synbio efforts but they generally have no idea of the pace of development, the opportunity of automation, and the general concept of DNA foundries as a way to power biotechnology apps.

There are already so many amazing companies in the synthetic biology space mainly in the US that the opportunities for the future are really very exciting. People are beginning to see that synthetic biology is biotechnology designed, engineered, and produced.

JOHN CUMBERS: You have a history with biotechnology and with promoting and developing synthetic biology, what are the most exciting developments you're seeing right now?

PAUL FREEMONT: I am really excited about applications that cell free synthetic biology offers. I should declare that my lab focuses on cell-free synbio but the idea that cell-free can actually offer a prototyping environment for synthetic biology applications is amazing.

Engineers that design planes have wind tunnels to test their designs and in the beginning chip designers had breadboards but biotechnologists had nothing so it's really cool that now there is cell-free platform to test biodesigns.

The other amazing app that cell free offers is in the development of paper based bio-sensors that can be used as point of care diagnostics or for field testing say of water or polluted soil. This is so cool because cell-free is really cheap and the biosensor designs are nucleic acid based so we can still design very cool genetic circuits but instead of running them in a cell we can do it cell free on paper. It's amazing. For low and middle income countries like those in Africa, cell-free detection systems offer huge advantages over existing methods for water purity, disease and industrial pollutants detection. To me, this is the number one coolest app for synbio but I am heavily biased—no apologies.

KARL SCHMIEDER: Do you think the application of creativity and innovation will advance the entire field of biotechnology?

PAUL FREEMONT: No question. Most innovation is happening at crossover points, at intersections between disciplines. I've seen some of that happening over the past five to ten years, but now it's accelerating.

The conversations between artists, architects, designers, engineers, biologists, life scientists, and computational scientists are driving innovation. People from different disciplines are exploring how to use and apply biotechnology in new ways that will drive new innovations and create new products.

I'm seeing this first-hand as a judge for the Bio Design Challenge and in my work with design students at the Royal College of Art in London.[20] I predict that in the next few years, most of the really cool innovations will come from these crossover points.

Whether that innovation penetrates the industrial dinosaurs remains to be seen but they will see new products coming to market from young and exciting companies that are using the new synthetic biology toolset. If big companies don't allow that kind of thinking to penetrate their cultures, they really do stand to lose.

JOHN CUMBERS: The first industries to use biotechnology were heavily regulated. Do you think regulatory processes kept people from applying design thinking to biotechnology?

PAUL FREEMONT: People like to argue that regulation prevents innovation. To some extent, it can when future processes and products that don't exist are over-regulated. On the other hand, regulation doesn't need to stifle innovation. Let me give you a few examples.

In agriculture, the industry is extraordinarily conservative with large multi-national monopolies that have inhibited innovation for years. You also have the pressure of the Non-Governmental Organizations (NGOs) and the anti-Genetically Modified Organism (GMO) folk who argue strongly against the monopolies and push the precautionary principle for all genetic engineering technologies—the EU has been particularly influenced by this as there are I believe no GM crops in Europe and little innovation in ag-biotechnology.

I personally would like to see more projects like Jim Hasselhof's OpenPlant initiative at Cambridge which is challenging this by creating open-source protocols for sharing in plant biotechnology.[21] By removing barriers to innovators in a highly monopolized industry will undoubtedly create innovation and this I hope will spur more acceptability of ag-biotech products by consumers.

The pharmaceutical industry is also very conservative. They're more open to innovation, but it's never been easy to convince large pharma companies to be early adopters of new technologies. There are too many internal vested interests. Today I think they are more open to innovation as their business model has been broken for several years and they are now looking to outsource some of their R&D or are creating internal innovation eco-systems. Pharma is good at manufacturing and marketing drugs but increasingly less good at innovation in terms of their R&D pipeline.

The chemical industry is probably the most conservative of the three. We tend to take commodity chemicals for granted but they are needed for almost all consumer products. In one sense, the industry is incredibly successful and there is a great deal of innovation in chemical engineering departments around the world. They're developing new ways to make chemical synthesis faster, cheaper, and cleaner. The scale of production is gigantic. So, while synbio and metabolic engineering can offer bio-based fermentation solutions for commodity chemical production, the economics don't stack up yet.

However, there is a realization that drop-in synbio solutions for more low volume high value chemical products is economically viable and once things like carbon and green taxes eventually penetrate the major chemical and oil industries, then they will all be scrambling for synbio and industrial biotechnology solutions. But it's not something the wider public is ever going to think about as long as they can still buy their products at affordable prices—does it matter how they are produced?

Traditional manufacturing industries haven't needed to make themselves more attractive or innovative. Maybe because they can't, maybe because they won't, or maybe because they don't need to. These industries will eventually be disrupted by biotechnology if we get the economic drivers and tax incentives right but given global politics at the moment I am not holding my breath.

I think in the short term synthetic biology could have its greatest impact on new types of consumer products—foods, fragrances, materials—items that people use every day. There is an opportunity to create new products designed and constructed with biology in a way that is sustainable and won't harm the environment. A lot of people, particularly millennials, really understand those ideas. It will bring more people into the field and also allow the public to understand the technology better.

KARL SCHMIEDER: How do you think regulations need to evolve as the systems created by synthetic biology become more complex?

PAUL FREEMONT: We need a mature debate on this. We know people are suspicious about the use of biotech on a mass scale. At the same time, we need regulations because we're working with living systems that are part of our everyday lives. We assume we can predict how engineered organisms will interact with so-called natural living systems but we can't—at least not yet so we really need to consider release synbio applications very seriously and openly.

If we achieve genetic designs of engineered organisms such that they don't impact on natural systems if released, then regulation will be straightforward. Until then, there will be uncertainties and doubts because biology is not predictable—it evolves, adapts and grows.

We want this technology to be immensely successful and sustainable. But there are enough people out there who want to preserve the natural world—whatever that is—and would prefer that synthetic biology and genetic engineering technologies do not succeed. Our environment of course is mostly not natural but man-made. It's in everyone's best interests to avoid a Three Mile Island [nuclear power plant] scenario that would kill the industry in its infancy.

The way I think we can do this is to be ambitious but not arrogant and to make safety and transparency as core planks of our research. If we have a mini-revolution around consumer biotech, then that will make the technology more accessible and I suspect this will have a huge impact on acceptability.

JOHN CUMBERS: In our interviews, Craig Venter called agriculture anti-nature. He suggested, we move to urban farming and let nature take its course. At the same time, from a food production point of view, we need to be as efficient as possible without destroying more forests and rainforests. How does consumer biotechnology help this?

PAUL FREEMONT: It offers an opportunity for young innovators and companies to work with artists, designers, and synthetic biologists. They provide an enormous vehicle for public learning about biotechnology. I know that's not necessarily their purpose, but they can spark curiosity and inspire more innovation so we get a whole flood of new consumer biotech products onto the market. Explaining our processes and motivations I think are key to this.

The technology then becomes extremely mainstream or at least more normal. People will say, "My shirt was made using these really cool engineered organisms," or "my jumper was dyed with a violet *E. coli* strain," or even "this great food was produced with biotech." It will be part of the conversation. There will be a language built around our understanding of biotechnology in the modern world. Synthetic biology language needs to be part of everyday conversation and everyone needs to engage. It is our responsibility to make sure everyone knows what the technology is, understands the opportunities and risks, and can engage in conversation and discussion.

KARL SCHMIEDER: Do you think the rise of the computer or IT industry hold lessons for consumer applications of synthetic biology?

PAUL FREEMONT: There are some. Every industry needs exemplars that people can look to. For example, I'm enamored with Bolt Threads and their first product, the spider silk tie. They are a pioneering company that is moving the whole consumer biotech industry forward. They're making the technology accessible to more people.

The pioneering consumer space in synthetic biology will ultimately lead to innovation in conservative industries as the public demands more sustainable products. That is important for the bioeconomy and the overall sustainability of the planet. The next generation [of consumers] are already fully engaged with the sustainability arguments.

The Internet industry has, to an extent, shown the benefits of being open and transparent but I think we can do better. For example, I'd like to see more distributed biological manufacturing units producing products related to local needs. That would be an amazing way to manufacture things, particularly materials. I love the example of the microbrewery industry. It has exploded not just in the United States, but all over the world. The technology that makes that possible—fermentation—is ripe for innovation and I would love to buy non-beer products along with beer at microbreweries.

I'd like to see fermentation-based manufacturing everywhere so that people could produce products anywhere using local feedstocks. That way, synthetic biology could be easily dropped into the microbrewery infrastructure everywhere.

Don't get me wrong, we need the big stuff as well. We need the big commodity chemical companies to adopt biology but I'd dearly love to see distributed biological manufacturing that is local and sustainable as a future way of living. Wouldn't that be really cool?

KARL SCHMIEDER: We will need an infrastructure to deliver biology as a service. That could be driven by microbreweries, but at what point do the brewers realize they can manufacture more than beer?

PAUL FREEMONT: Big companies won't drive that. Big companies have a deep knowledge of fermentation technology which is not trivial, but the economic drivers and incentives are not yet in place for product pivots. However, local small-scale fermentation technology is ripe for innovation.

Entrepreneurs and the next generation of synthetic biologists will be attracted to this as the technology basically hasn't changed much in thousands of years. There are many exciting places for innovation in that space, particularly in terms of energy sources and savings, using waste streams for feedstock, improving the predictability of scaling production using engineered organisms. People will see real opportunities and it could be very exciting.

Again, this leads to the idea of consumer biotech, where you get consumer products, the fragrances and flavors, the textiles and leather coming from the local biological production or even microbrewery which expands its product offering. You could start with craft-based products created through distributed biological manufacturing. There's no reason why a craft synthetic biology industry can't develop and thrive, particularly around big metropolitan areas.

I can see all of this happening as people embrace the technology along with making sure that people understand the possibilities, opportunities and risks. We absolutely need to expose society at large to synbio and biotechnology to help them see the possibilities and opportunities and also to allow them to express their desires and hopes and visions for a more sustainable world.

CHRISTINA AGAPAKIS: THE PRODUCT IS LIFE ITSELF

CHRISTINA AGAPAKIS, Ph.D., is the creative director at Ginkgo BioWorks, an organism design company bringing biology to industrial engineering. As a biologist, writer, and artist, Christina has collaborated with engineers, designers, artists, and social scientists to explore the unexpected connections between microbiology, technology, art, and popular culture.

KARL SCHMIEDER: Along with Suzanne Lee of Modern Meadow, you're one of two creative directors at biotechnology companies, why is that role important?

CHRISTINA AGAPAKIS: Both Suzanne and I have creative leadership roles at our companies. It's a lot more than being in charge of the PowerPoint slides, which I do on occasion. It's about thinking deeply and differently about the interface between the technology and society.

I ask questions like, "How does this technology live in the real world? Will it meet a real human need? How will we present it to the world? How will it be tangible? How do we imagine that future? What story do we need to tell about that future?"

Asking those deep questions is valuable when you're talking about bringing new technology to life, especially when the product can be life itself.

KARL SCHMIEDER: Should other biotechnology companies consider having a designer on staff?

CHRISTINA AGAPAKIS: I think it's really important for us to engage with design. I've taught designers in art schools about synthetic biology and it was a really amazing experience to see this technology through a designer's eyes and through their questions. They're being trained to ask questions with an openness that opens up a lot of interesting new directions and a criticality that challenges us to ask if things could be different. That approach is very powerful.

We should be critical of the technologies we create and questioning of how they will be used. These questions can inform the stories we tell and shape the next generation of design.

KARL SCHMIEDER: Do you think anyone has done this successfully? Some Silicon Valley companies claim to do this but design or transparency haven't been a part of the biotechnology industry.

CHRISTINA AGAPAKIS: I don't think so but maybe we need to ask what constitutes success? New technologies are complex. They're shaped by cultural forces. Engaging with those forces is important. I'm not sure that means we'll be successful but it is necessary.

A lot of the synthetic biology story has been something like, in the future we'll be able to do this kind of thing with biology. That story is convincing enough to get thousands of students to participate in the International Genetically Engineered Machine (iGEM) competition every year. It's convincing enough for graduate students to spend five years thinking about these questions. It's convincing enough to get investors or customers to put their money behind the idea of engineering biology.

Creating the provocations to spark imaginations, to imagine what is enabled by the technology is incredibly important. It's a reason to engage with a larger group who can imagine these things with us. If we are saying we are re-imaging life itself, that should be a really big conversation that we have with different audiences understanding that each will have a different level of knowledge and different level of skepticism.

Customers and the media are looking for something tangible. They want to see how the technology works and how it affects them. Customers with complex supply chains want to know how it will affect them, how it changes the cost of things, how it changes production. Not to mention that it's safe and done in a way that is ethical and aligns with their values.

KARL SCHMIEDER: The impact of biotechnology on consumers has been largely invisible, how do you think that will change as companies make it more public?

CHRISTINA AGAPAKIS: It's true. You don't hear the splashy story behind the enzymes in your dishwasher detergent. You don't hear much about the bio manufacturing of everyday goods. Or the stories of the industrial biotech companies making the amino acids necessary for animal feeds.

It's been interesting to see a new kind of consumer-facing biotech story emerging recently, showing how biotechnology is making an impact not just in the pharmaceutical industry or in ingredient supply chains but around creativity and the design of everyday products.

At the 2016 Biofabricate conference, Adidas unveiled a sneaker made from bio-engineered spider silk.[22] The genetic engineering was the driving force for telling this consumer-facing story. It was a biotechnology product but the unveiling looked like an Apple product launch with this amazing enthusiasm. Bolt Threads just did this with the launch of their spider silk tie too.

People are waiting for consumer products driven by a biotech story. Products that place their biotech stories front and center are differentiating themselves. It opens up a new world and changes the narrative around GMOs.

KARL SCHMIEDER: I'm inspired by Patagonia's deal with Bolt Threads, given that they've always told a very strong anti-GMO story. At the same time, they're looking to create sustainable products with high performance characteristics, so brewed materials can become part of their narrative

CHRISTINA AGAPAKIS: There is something deeper going on around engagement and education. Our community relies on a lot of assumptions about anti-GMO opinions. I think we need to understand how and why people think about GMOs the way that they do before we can try to educate them.

People don't see GMOs as just one thing. There are a lot of nuances in that community because of the way GMOs have been deployed historically. People often have quite specific views about what they are opposed to, whether it has to do with agricultural practices, intellectual property, or something else.

What it's really about is values. If you can talk about values in addition to facts, then you can create a very different dialogue.

Scientists often have a naive idea that if we educate people on facts, then they will agree with us. But the way people come to understand the world is complicated. Dan Kahan at Yale has shown that the more facts people know about science, the more likely they are to disagree based on their ideological position. That's pretty discouraging, but he's also shown that if you look at scientific curiosity, the more curious someone is the more likely they are to hold opinions that counter their ideological point of view. They're more willing to think differently about the world.

I'm much more interested in how you can improve scientific curiosity? How do you spark people's passions and emotions? How do you get people invested? Literacy feels boring and didactic. Scientists aren't just about facts. We might rationalize things after the fact, but we often start with an obsession, a passion for answering a question.

KARL SCHMIEDER: How does synthetic biology impact supply chains?

CHRISTINA AGAPAKIS: Supply chains are very complex. For example, for foods and fragrances, many ingredients come from agriculture. Farmers grow fields of flowers that are harvested. The flowers are pressed, oils extracted, and fragrances distilled.

Many other ingredients are also produced chemically starting with petroleum, and there is a growing number of products manufactured using fermentation or biocatalysis—products created from natural sources and enzymes.

Synthetic biology can improve strains and enzymes to make those bio-catalyzed products more efficiently. You can start with fewer inputs to get the final output. Or you could design new strains to replace agriculturally- or petroleum-derived ingredients. That could stabilize the supply chain so you're no longer dependent on growing cycles, protect yourself from price fluctuations, and increase sustainability.

Synthetic biology, depending on how it's done, can be more sustainable and renewable. That's the dream of having a bio-based economy—not just for flavors and fragrances—but for all other industries.

One of the things that still needs to be figured out is how to make synthetic biology more accessible. What will happen when costs go down further and more industries and products can use biotechnology? What will happen when biological manufacturing is available everywhere? Not just used by multinational corporations in the global North, but in other places, in their own context, to drive growth and change.

KARL SCHMIEDER: Where do you think synthetic biology will be in a 30 years?

CHRISTINA AGAPAKIS: I don't like that question because I know I'll be wrong! It's so hard to predict what the impact of a technology might be that far in the future. The clichés are that no one making the first cars could have predicted traffic jams, and no one building the early internet could have predicted social media.

Of course this kind of speculation is also valuable to understand what's going on today, even if we can't foresee the future. I know that in thirty years biology will be much more important for many industries. It's going to be an essential part of a lot of things that we just can't predict at this point.

I'd like to see more people engaging with the ideas of engineered biology. I'd like to see people as excited about the technology and the possibilities as we are. Thinking about and engaging with the bacteria that live on us in new ways. Thinking of our own bodies as ecosystems and being able to engage with that in a meaningful way.

I'd like to see a cultural change around genetics and DNA that is less deterministic and has some of the nuances that scientists live with daily. At the same time, I'd like to move away from those very dangerous stories that tell us how DNA determines who we are and what we do. That's not how DNA works. There isn't a single gene for creativity or beauty. All of these things are complicated biologically and culturally.

Right now, I'd like to have more companies and consumers asking, "Where does my stuff come from? How is it made? And, can we imagine a way that is more sustainable and unbounded by current technological limitations?" That would be fascinating and potentially very productive for any company to ask.

SECTION 2. THE TOOLS, SOFTWARE, AND ARTIFICIAL INTELLIGENCE MAKING BIOTECHNOLOGY ACCESSIBLE

FUTURIST RAY KURZWEIL HAS MADE headlines with his provocative, yet often accurate predictions. Author of bestselling books like *The Age of Spiritual Machines, The Singularity Is Near*, and *How to Create a Mind*, Kurzweil has accurately predicted the availability of a wide range of personal computers, the ubiquity of high-bandwidth internet, and self-driving cars.

In a 2001, Kurzweil wrote *"The Law of Accelerating Returns"* an essay which states that "fundamental measures of technology follow predictable and exponential trajectories."

The most famous example is Moore's Law, named after Intel co-founder, Gordon Moore.

In 1965, Moore predicted, "the number of transistors incorporated into a chip will approximately double every 24 months." For the past four decades, Moore's Law has held true: computers have shrunk from filling a room to filling your pocket, becoming more powerful along the way.

Over the past five decades, biologists have become experts at reading and writing DNA. Both have largely become a digital endeavor.

In 2006, University of Washington researcher Rob Carlson (who you will meet in this section), described the rate of sequencing DNA or cost per sequenced base as a function of time. That cost has fallen from about $1 per base pair in the mid-1990s to a tenth of a cent in 2008. The cost of writing DNA, or gene synthesis, has declined from more than $10 per base to less than one cent per base today. Declines in the costs of reading and writing DNA recall Moore's Law. The curves plotting the exponential drops in DNA reading and writing costs have been called The Carlson Curve.

Software is changing the practice of biology. Until very recently, biology had been conducted by researchers working with their hands at lab benches. That model hasn't changed much since before the Industrial Revolution. The smartest people in biology still do the manual labor. The impact of doing things this way is significant—it takes longer to achieve meaningful results because experiments can only be conducted in sequence and reproducibility must be established.

But now, instead of conducting one experiment at a lab bench, life scientists can write a computer program. When they wish to share the experiment, they just send a copy of the program and rerun it.

The digitization of biology will facilitate the creation of new organisms able to produce chemicals, foods, and medicines. It will make it easier to create organisms that respond to their environment, and eventually, will make it easy to create multi-cellular organisms. Perhaps most profoundly, the digitization of biology is resulting in Kurzweil's "exponential trajectories."

In this section, you'll read interviews with the hardware and software tool developers who are democratizing biotechnology, making it more accessible and reproducible. We've included interviews with entrepreneurs who are using bio-fabrication techniques (with and without genetic engineering) to create novel materials and disrupt trillion-dollar industries. These innovators are showing us what is possible with synthetic biology right now.

ROB CARLSON: YOU'LL SOON BE USING SYNTHETIC BIOLOGY TO MANUFACTURE EVERYTHING

DIGITAL TECHNOLOGIES AND ROBOTICS ARE transforming manufacturing. In fact, according to Lisa Caldwell, EY Americas Advisory Industrial Products Lead, "the advanced manufacturing technology revolution has only just begun." Digital and robotics are only part of the manufacturing revolution and synthetic biology's impact on manufacturing is only just getting started. To understand how, we reached out to Rob Carlson, author of *Biology is Technology*. Rob is one of the world's leading experts on synthetic biology and in 2001 published an essay in *The Economist* titled, *"The World in 2050,"*[23] where he first mentioned "distributed biological manufacturing."

JOHN CUMBERS: You've been involved in synthetic biology since its earliest days, can you describe how tools are changing to make it accessible?

ROB CARLSON: Our world today is largely the result of a tool stack that reaches from computer-aided design (CAD) on a laptop screen to machines that manufacture products. A suite of computer applications and application program interfaces (APIs) makes it easy to take a design from a laptop, move atoms around with a printer, make stuff, and ship it out the door.

The Economist just published an article on a motorcycle company that went from whiteboard to a complex, manufactured product in less than three years.[24] That's quite fast for a motor vehicle. Computer-aided design, engineering, and simulation systems made it possible to create and test the motorcycle long before anything physical was built.

When I was writing *Biology is Technology*, I started using the Honda Element commercial as an example of integrated design for manufacturing. It shows thousands of Lego building blocks coming together to form the Honda.

The narrator says, "Every piece has a purpose." What he doesn't say is that Honda can—and you can—simulate them all before you build.

The design-build-test cycle is so well understood for most products of mechanical and electrical engineering that in many instances you can go straight from simulation to manufacturing. Boeing did this to design and build the 777—the first commercial airline designed and tested entirely on a computer. Boeing built the first airframe and a test pilot flew it straight away.

Biology is different. The fundamental ability to apply design and automation to gene and genome design has been missing until now. To engineer a cell and scale its growth to produce a product required designing dozens of experiments with hundreds of parameters at the same time. It had to be done precisely to be reproducible but it was all done manually, which impeded reproducibility. Until recently, biotechnology had no tool stack. You couldn't transfer what works for designing and manufacturing motorcycles or airplanes to biology.

KARL SCHMIEDER: Do you think the technologies we need to get into place for biological manufacturing are maturing?

ROB CARLSON: Yes, three things in particular have changed recently.

First, is the development and deployment of quality systems in biological manufacturing. These are common in many other kinds of industries, but outside of pharmaceutical manufacturing they have been rare in biotech.

Second, is the recent arrival of design for manufacturing in biology. We aren't at the point where you can design a new organism on a laptop, simulate it, send the manufacturing instructions to automated prototyping instrumentation, then ship that recipe off to manufacturing. But those pieces are coming together much faster than I expected just a few years ago.

Third, it is now possible to design enzymes with new functions and to design new enzymatic pathways that can be used to make entirely new products.

When you put these three developments together, then you start to see how biology fits into the engineering infrastructure that underlies the rest of our economy. Again, we have a lot of work to do to realize the final capability, but the pieces work, and they are coming together.

KARL SCHMIEDER: Do you have any examples?

ROB CARLSON: Amyris,[25] one of the first synthetic biology companies, started by focusing on mass-producing artemisinin to treat malaria. They expanded into bio-fuels, faced down several challenges, and came out of the bio-fuels hangover in a much better position—at least as far as their technical capabilities are concerned. The Amyris team was forced to develop many version 1.0 bioengineering tools.

Today, they have the experience and capability to roll out many projects, and their 2016 agreement[26] with Ginkgo BioWorks[27] shows that Amyris is interested in expanding access to their now-sophisticated manufacturing capacity. They have made a great deal of progress in being able to iterate design, build, and test by automating their engineering processes.

Through years of development and learning, Amyris experienced a few bumps in the road, resulting in a diaspora of talented people who are now taking what they learned there to the next level.

Tim Gardner[28] is a pioneer in the field of synthetic biology and a former employee of Amyris. There, he cobbled together their quality systems from whatever software was available at the time. He left and founded Riffyn[29] to build a design studio and research and development platform from scratch. It's a system that enables quality by design. The software dramatically improves reproducibility. It's analogous to Six Sigma, the management techniques used across all manufacturing to improve business processes.

Riffyn is a Github[30] for biological manufacturing processes. It allows easy version tracking of processes and lets companies or individuals take a research and development or manufacturing process that works in one place and transfer it to another.

This helps address tech transfer hiccups that frequently crop up during mergers and acquisitions. For example, Roche recently eliminated Genentech's manufacturing in South San Francisco and now has to enable that capability in other locations. R&D will still be conducted at Genentech HQ, but the manufacturing will be done elsewhere.

How do you communicate the manufacturing process from HQ to wherever the product will actually get made? Currently, that is all done manually for biotech products.

JOHN CUMBERS: Many companies are great at engineering bugs to produce a product but few are great at scaling production. How do they overcome that challenge?

ROB CARLSON: They outsource because scale-up and manufacturing are expensive. However, in outsourcing, they can lose ownership of the manufacturing process. Bringing that process back in-house requires the ability to wrangle automation and genetics at the same time, which brings us to the arrival of design for manufacturing in biotechnology.

Let me give you another example: Synthace's[31] Antha is a programming language for biology and an operating system for labs. Antha allows you to go from the white-board all the way to automated measurement and manufacturing. Antha gives users clear and complete instructions and allows them to execute on hardware from many vendors. It's really an operating system that links the research laboratory to the manufacturing plant.

Synthace is working on drivers for everything from automated cell culture systems to liquid handlers, from PCR machines to mass spectrometers. At the core of Antha is a "multifactorial design of experiments" philosophy that treats all the settings on all these instruments, as well as all the genetic and physiological features of engineered organisms, as parameters that can be rapidly optimized in parallel.

Ultimately, Antha allows users to better manage manufacturing lines better. It is biological engineering the way you would hope it would be.

KARL SCHMIEDER: How does all this software and infrastructure impact the biological engineering?

ROB CARLSON: It will accelerate it. Having all this software in one place will make the engineering of biology and manufacturing scale-up much easier. Design the pathway, prototype, then design the manufacturing process. You can hand off your engineered microorganism and processes to a manufacturing facility and they will boot it up and start producing.

KARL SCHMIEDER: Does that bring us closer to your vision of distributed biological manufacturing?

ROB CARLSON: One step closer. The next major development that will bring distributed biological process closer to reality is the design of enzymes and pathways that can use local feedstocks to produce end-products.

Standard synthetic chemistry has provided a zoo of molecules that are the building blocks of the modern economy. Many products today are possible only through the properties of molecules that are entirely designed and manufactured by humans. Synthetic chemistry—through plastics, coatings or catalysts—synthetic chemistry literally transforms our world.

But of all the materials we can theoretically imagine, synthetic chemistry can only manufacture a fraction. Enzymes, however, can manage feats of chemistry that provide access to a much larger number of potential materials.

JOHN CUMBERS: Do you have any examples?

ROB CARLSON: The Defense Advanced Research Projects Agency (DARPA) has a project underway to extend this capability by employing novel combinations of enzymes to build a thousand materials that have never existed before. Moreover, after a century of effort, we have learned enough biochemistry to start designing new enzymes with new capabilities, that expand even further the accessible gamut of the materials spectrum.

This has already been demonstrated on a small scale, and largely without access to the tools that companies like Riffyn and Synthace are building. Imagine what will be possible when all these capabilities are brought together.

In a few years, we will have the ability to design enzymatic pathways that use the most economically viable feedstocks to make products for whatever markets we want to focus on. Coupling pathway design to test, measurement, and prototyping, then finally to manufacturing processes, will be very powerful economically.

KARL SCHMIEDER: You've written about the importance of microbreweries in the growth of the bioeconomy, why are they important?

ROB CARLSON: Microbrewing teaches us that distributed biological manufacturing is not only possible, but also that it can compete against large, centralized manufacturing. This is with a product—beer—that is basically water, and worth only a few dollars a liter.

In contrast, there are plenty of compounds worth tens, hundreds, or even thousands of dollars a liter that are now derived from a barrel of oil. When those products can be brewed the way beer is, then distributed biological manufacturing will work even better.

Now, if you have the ability to describe those organisms and manufacturing processes in software—using a combination of something like Riffyn and Antha—then you enable a new kind of business altogether. This will allow us to develop and version processes, and communicate and license those processes.

We'll see new companies that have the option to develop and license processes rather than only to manufacture products, which would bring biology closer to the way the rest of the economy works. This is only possible when you have the full bioengineering tool stack at your disposal.

JOHN CUMBERS: How will distributed biological manufacturing evolve?

ROB CARLSON: The early wins in biology are coming from embracing what biotechnology already does best: Building bugs [microorganisms] that produce valuable molecules that can be grown at scale and with the flexibility of brewing beer. At the moment, because it is early and the tools are still new and a bit expensive, only large players operating in large markets can make effective use of these tools.

Zymergen[32] has its own homegrown tool stack and is seeing enormous success in optimizing production pathways for its customers, who own microbes that already generate many billions in revenues from chemicals. Over time, the technology will diffuse out into the larger bioengineering community, which will support an increasingly diverse array of biologically manufactured products.

Eventually, the market will decide how any given product is produced and at what scale. We already know that biological manufacturing works in that it can outcompete high-end petroleum products even at today's prices. As the technology matures, it seems likely that brewing will be the future of biomanufacturing. Where the micro-brewing of chemicals makes sense, that's what people will do.

Ultimately, you'll be able to scale production to meet local demand, while generating a profit at whatever scale works in your market. This was the core of my distributed biological manufacturing hypothesis 15 years ago and it is starting to be realized.

EMILY LEPROUST: ACCELERATING SYNTHESIS OF LIFE'S BUILDING BLOCKS

DNA IS THE OPERATING CODE for life on earth. Creating new materials, hardier crops, and innovative medicines requires massive numbers of carefully designed synthetic DNA sequences. In 2013, Emily Leproust, Ph.D., cofounded Twist Bioscience with Bill Peck and Bill Banyai to improve and accelerate DNA synthesis. Emily was an early pioneer in synthesizing long strands of DNA. In 2015, she was selected by *Foreign Policy* as one of its 100 Leading Global Thinkers of 2015 for fast-tracking the building blocks of life.[33]

JOHN CUMBERS: Could you tell us Twist's origin story?

EMILY LEPROUST: Twist's original mission was to make molecular cloning obsolete.

When we started the company, researchers were not happy with their options for ordering genes, gene manufacturing took too long, and DNA was expensive. Since scientists generally have more ideas than money, expensive DNA prevented them from conducting their experiments.

We thought that by re-inventing DNA synthesis, we could turn unhappy customers into happy customers. We could create and grow a more vibrant market and a very successful business.

Over time, we've expanded the DNA synthesis platform beyond genes. New applications are changing our business faster than we anticipated. We now support pharmaceutical drug development and data storage with our products. As a result, our strategy is evolving to capture exciting new market opportunities.

KARL SCHMIEDER: The DNA synthesis market is estimated at a billion dollars but the price of synthesis continues to drop. How do you create value if prices are dropping?

EMILY LEPROUST: Writing DNA or DNA synthesis is an elastic market. When you lower the price, you grow the market because people can perform more experiments and you enable new applications.

DNA sequencing is a useful analogy. In 2009, you could conduct whole genome sequencing but it was expensive. By 2010-2011, next generation sequencing became cheap enough to make it accessible. By 2016, you could start sequencing the microbiome. You couldn't imagine sequencing the microbiome in 2009 because it was too expensive.

The same thing is happening with DNA synthesis. As prices decrease, buyers can go through the design-test-build cycles faster. Experiments will no longer be limited by price. The market expands.

When people can afford unlimited amounts of DNA, the answers to their questions will improve. Budgets will grow. Makers will stop cloning in-house. At that point, we enable completely new applications. Synthetic biology will be limited only by imagination and creativity.

In the not-too-distant future, I believe researchers will be able to make a bacterium from scratch affordably. Today, it would cost millions of dollars. The market is non-existent. If we could make *E. coli* for a few thousand dollars—or even tens of thousands of dollars—the market would explode.

JOHN CUMBERS: Could you explain how research will change when synthetic DNA is cheap and readily available?

EMILY LEPROUST: Until recently, scientists limited the design of their experiments because DNA was expensive and creating variants was hard work. It was a form of self-censorship. If they knew they could only create five variants in a week, they would only create five.

As researchers realize they can get unlimited amounts of DNA inexpensively, they're more likely to reimagine the science. They will broaden the scope of their experiments. We're already seeing this.

At Twist, we're improving software and hardware automation, making it easier and more efficient for scientists to access DNA sequences that would otherwise remain sequestered in their imagination. In the long run, that means biology will become more of a software or data discipline, which we are already seeing in sequencing. Scientists will spend more time using software to design their genes and organisms, and they'll outsource the synthesis to Twist. The increase in demand will allow us to lower costs and continue to deliver value, with research as a whole becoming more efficient and cost effective.

KARL SCHMIEDER: What do you think non-biotech businesses need to understand about synthetic biology and the impact it might have on their business?

EMILY LEPROUST: At a high level, they need to understand biology is coming and it is impacting all areas of life and business.

We're living in the biotech century. In the 1950s, you could create value in aerospace. In the 1970s, it was semiconductors. In the 1980s, it was computers and the internet. We're now in the century of biology. Businesses need to be prepared to enter, embrace, and leverage biology for the good of their business and the good of the planet.

Plastics, for example, are made of materials that are largely manufactured from oil. Plastics brought tremendous benefits to the world but they're not sustainable. With biology, we will be able to make the same chemicals without oil in a way that is sustainable. In many ways, that's the low-hanging fruit.

In the next 25 years, you're going to see revolutions in materials that spans mycelium being used to replace polystyrene to spider silk replacing nylon. Materials are being revolutionized by proteins engineered to have a specific function. Researchers are able to use the massive amount of synthetic DNA complexity offered by Twist Bioscience to rapidly engineer these new protein functions.

You're already seeing advances in healthcare. Knowledge of biology in cancer, for example, allows you to personalize treatments. We'll be able to increase our longevity and the quality of our lives. Engineered biology moves us into personalized medicines.

The changes to the food industry will improve sustainability and food will taste the way it's meant to taste. I think we'd all like food that is grown sustainably with fewer chemicals, tastes great, and doesn't spoil as fast.

In the next several years, using DNA for data storage will become a very real possibility. Data storage is a $10 billion to $15 billion market and growing rapidly. DNA provides several benefits over current storage methods. It is stable for thousands of years. It allows density of data storage—all the world's digital data could be stored in one shoebox of DNA. It has low energy requirements. Facilities today require significant energy to preserve data. It's also a universal format. DNA is composed of four bases. That will be true for all time. Twist has a non-exclusive collaboration with Microsoft and the University of Washington that has demonstrated the feasibility and benefits of DNA as a storage media.

Biology is here. It is impacting all areas of our lives and will help solve significant problems. If you're a company and you're not prepared, you will not benefit from the changes. It's unstoppable and it's for the better.

TIM FELL: CLOUD BIOLOGY IS TRANSFORMING THE LIFE SCIENCES

TIM FELL PH.D., HAS WORKED in biotechnology as a founding entrepreneur at a DNA microarray tools company and an epigenetics drug discovery company. Before that, he spent 13 years performing interdisciplinary research in the departments of biochemistry, engineering and materials at the University of Oxford. Tim is the CEO of Synthace, a company that started as a synthetic biology company but pivoted to create software tools to make the practice of biology more effective.

KARL SCHMIEDER: How did you pivot from biotechnology to software company?

TIM FELL: We quickly realized that the in-house software tools we were developing were actually more impactful and valuable than the products we were trying to create with them, so we pivoted.

As a software company, Synthace is focussed on increasing productivity in the life sciences. Our cloud-based operating system for biology, Antha, links lab equipment, protocols, and processes in a way that only software can. It makes it easy to design and optimize laboratory workflows that are reliable, shareable, and even saleable.

JOHN CUMBERS: How will Antha change life sciences research?

TIM FELL: We sit at the nexus of four emerging network effects. First, laboratory protocols will be created and shared like smartphone apps.

Right now, experiments are run in different ways by different scientists. If you want to reproduce someone's work, you need to look up the methods section of a scientific paper.

Unfortunately, those instructions are usually only a paragraph long and don't contain all the important details, meaning you largely need to guess how they did it. You spend eight weeks trying to recreate a protocol and often end up failing.

Protocols should be easy to exchange and run and most importantly they should work. Antha codifies them as software that can be shared at the click of a mouse. Instead of a protocol being peer-reviewed by only a few people before it's published in a journal, it can be reviewed by the community. It will be far more accessible. You will be able to code a method in a few hours and upload it to something like the app store. You can give it away or charge whatever you want for it.

This gives researchers the ability to share their working practices easily. Instead of publishing their protocols once a year or so, they can do it weekly. This will accelerate research because better protocols lead to better results and better results lead to better understanding.

Second, automated laboratory equipment use will increase dramatically. Today, 35 billion dollars' worth of laboratory equipment is purchased every year. With the exception of DNA sequencing, it's a fragmented market where no one company has more than 20 percent market share and the intense competition has hampered the development of standards.

Every instrument uses different software and they don't talk to each other. Interfaces are unintuitive and as a result, when you walk into a lab you'll see most machines aren't being used. Too often they are bought and programmed for one experiment and then sit in idle isolation. Utilization is commonly under 10 percent.

Those instruments should be in use all the time. They should be easy to program, connect together and schedule jobs to.

The Antha operating system is independent of and doesn't compete with the instrument manufacturers, rather it enhances their hardware's utility. Crucially, it works interoperably across platforms, meaning protocols can be run on any equipment enabled with an Antha driver. It makes it easy to program laboratory equipment allowing researchers to automate their workflows and perform experiments at scale. It generates traceable, reproducible data and ends up increasing the utility of existing equipment and driving demand for more automation.

Third, laboratory reagents will be highly-characterized and optimized for automation. Scientists used to make their own buffers. I remember the day somebody first bought a kit from Sigma-Aldrich for our lab and we asked, "What's that?" We laughed because it cost $50 for a solution that we could mix ourselves. A year later, the shelves were full of kits. We realized we weren't just buying the liquids, we were buying a set of instructions that came with the kit that assured us our experiment would work if we followed the directions.

Today, kit manufacturers are developing kits for 96- and 384-well plates. But the set of instructions for a 96 or 384-well plate is too complex to be printed on a piece of paper—it has to be software. That's another element of the Antha OS.

Antha allows reagent manufacturers to create direct integrations with the machines in the lab and supply reagents in large array formats with highly optimized protocols that are software.

This means scientists no longer have to worry about intricate experimental details, which software is much more reliable at determining. They can now concentrate on the scientific questions they want to ask, leaving the Antha OS to work out all the low level details associated with planning, ordering reagents and executing the complex experiments they need to do.

Fourth, scientific data collection and analysis will improve. Many scientists still take notes by hand. Whether they use a physical or electronic notebook, they're jotting down what they think after the experiment takes place. The data they collect is unstructured.

In contrast, an Antha workflow has all the parameters to be measured coded upfront and so the data is automatically collected. It is very simple to add additional experimental factors and link appropriate sensors to measure them—the time, the temperature, humidity, gas concentrations and pressures, ambient light etc.—to collect time-structured logs of everything. You get a comprehensive picture of the entire experiment.

Once you have that data, you can apply machine learning to look at the complexities and patterns that our human brains are unable to see. Biology is too complex for us to see everything.

Software abstraction is key to being able to properly engineer biology. I am convinced this is going to be highly disruptive to the life sciences and to tell you the truth, that's why we are so excited by it.

KARL SCHMIEDER: Do you think companies need a bio strategy?

TIM FELL: Yes, absolutely. It's very important. There are huge opportunities because when it comes to making complex products biology is more efficient than other manufacturing technologies for. It is also easily distributed and it's green. That said, biosecurity needs to be a part of the conversation. Whether that means securing your biological data or being able to rapidly respond to a biological risk, both should be on people's minds.

.

TIM GARDNER: BIOLOGICAL SYSTEMS CAN SOLVE NEARLY ANY PHYSICAL CHALLENGE

AMONG THE PEOPLE MAKING BIOLOGY easier to engineer, Tim Gardner stands out. Along with his Ph.D. supervisor Jim Collins at Boston University, he wrote one of the seminal papers in the field in 2000, Construction of a genetic toggle switch in *Escherichia coli*—a functional biological switch, made from genetic parts. Later, while at the integrated renewable products company, Amyris, he led the engineering of yeast strains and pioneered process technologies for the large-scale bio-manufacturing of renewable chemicals. He then founded Riffyn to accelerate innovation in research and development.

KARL SCHMIEDER: Tell us how you started Riffyn?

TIM GARDNER: I've worked in biotech for twenty years as a student, academic researcher, and founder. I held leadership positions in medical and industrial companies. Time and time again, I kept running into horrible research and development inefficiencies. By that, I mean it takes too long to get products to market. There are too many errors and mistakes and too much effort wasted on fundamentally unproductive pursuits.

The science is hard and biology is complex, but researchers are also blocked by the challenges of communicating scientific results and information to each other in reproducible, scientific methodologies.

Scientists are still relying on a means of communication that was developed 400 years ago for a handful of people that had regular contact to debate narrow ideas. That eventually evolved into publications. Today, it's presentations and spreadsheets that are inadequate for communicating complex, sophisticated ideas.

As a result, people don't have a clear understanding of what their colleagues are doing, how they're doing it, and whether the results are trustworthy. The bottom line is people make bad decisions because they don't have adequate information to make good ones.

I started Riffyn to solve this with computer aided design (CAD), statistical data, and an analytics approach to science experimentation. That way, you start at designing an experiment, improving it iteratively, and communicating it as structured, unambiguous, visual data based on real-time data acquisition. Riffyn tells you how an experimental design is working, helps you make it better, and assures you get the results you want so that anyone can look at your data and get the same results. This is the same way you would design parts for a car.

We believe the impact is significant. We have examples where we can cut time to market in half and double the productivity of R&D organizations. When you do that, you reduce the capital expenditures on new products and you increase the certainty that you'll get a better result.

JOHN CUMBERS: How does Riffyn impact an R&D organization?

TIM GARDNER: When business decision-makers have to decide whether to invest in a new product, they look at time and investment. If they know they can develop a biological product in two years with a million-dollar investment, they're more likely to build that product. If it's going to take four years and cost $10 million, they're never going to make that product—especially since it might cost five times as much when they factor in uncertainty. They'll never get their return on investment.

To increase the size of the bioeconomy, substituting bio-based products for those that would be made from chemistry and petroleum, we need to reduce the cost of developing those products. If we can do that, then developing more specialized products is acceptable. We'll stop looking for the billion dollar blockbusters, which are few and far between. We'll have a lot more entrepreneurial success and investors will be happy because we're delivering on the promise of the biotechnology.

KARL SCHMIEDER: Can you give us more details on what Riffyn enables?

TIM GARDNER: Riffyn integrates data from people, instruments, automation systems, databases, spreadsheets—anywhere you're capturing data. We take all that data and organize it around your experimental design processes.

Right now, we don't control robots or provide automation, but we have an application programming interface (API) that facilitates automated workflows. Our idea isn't to automate the world, it's to ensure the capital investments you've made are working more efficiently and all the data is captured in a uniform, repeatable structure. For us, that results in a software system oriented toward the scientists in a lab and the director, not toward automation.

Our thesis is that the solution to faster, better, cheaper drugs, and faster, better, cheaper bio-based products is predictability of information. It's about integrating information and making better informed decisions. It's not necessarily about fancy robots or magical tools.

JOHN CUMBERS: It sounds like you're taking both a scientific and engineering approach to solve a problem.

TIM GARDNER: I've always taken an engineering approach to science. But I think it's hubris to think engineers can approach science without learning how science works, or how a scientist works. I also think scientists miss a lot of opportunities by not learning engineering.

JOHN CUMBERS: People often compare the tech industry to the biotech industry. The tech industry started with hardcore science. Creating the microprocessor, you could argue, was a scientific challenge. You could call the explosion of computing and the internet, 95 percent engineering. The economic value of the 1960s through the 1990s could be credited to a boom in engineering. When you now look at Google, Facebook, Netflix and Palantir, the need is for scientists—data scientists and statisticians. The tech industry is now going back to science—big data, machine learning, analytics. I wonder if we'll see the same thing with biology. We're now hitting the period that requires engineering. We'll see productivity gains and a lot of great things made with less science involved. Then we'll swing back toward a period of science and analytics to build on top of that.

TIM GARDNER: You make a great observation. Engineering has more science in it than people realize. The idea that scientists are being paid more or are delivering more value or are in greater demand is not entirely true. It's hard to hire engineers. Value tends to accrue to people and organizations that can reduce uncertainty.

The place where you can do magic is where you clear the cloud of uncertainty and turn that into something usable. That's why data scientists are in demand and hold such a powerful role. They have the potential to reduce uncertainty.

I would argue that a lot of engineering is more empirical than we give it credit. There's a lot of experimentation that goes on in engineering. The airplane might be viewed as an engineering problem but Orville and Wilbur [Wright] were performing fluid dynamics experiments to understand how to engineer a propeller in a wing. My hope is not that you see science take over engineering or that engineering takes over science, but that you see the synthesis of them.

KARL SCHMIEDER: What do you think non-biotech businesses need to know about synthetic biology?

TIM GARDNER: When it comes to health and you're solving a biological problem, you need to know biology. The environment is also a biological system. If you don't understand the nitrogen cycle and the transformation of matter by biological processes, you can't come up with good solutions to environmental problems. Most laymen should know there is no physical problem that a biological system hasn't solved.

Let's take the most extreme example, radiodurans, an organism that can absorb the radiation equivalent of a nuclear blast. It's a poly-extremophile. When it absorbs radiation, it shreds its genome into tiny fragments then stitches back together to keep going.

There are organisms that can detect light or transform electricity into energy for survival. Compared to the hydraulics or batteries that you might put into a robot, muscles are incredibly efficient. It's extraordinary.

If we want to use those properties to make the world a more efficient, higher performing, more enjoyable place, then we need to learn from nature.

BETHAN WOLFENDEN: SYNTHETIC BIOLOGY'S HARDWARE SHOULD BE ACCESSIBLE

SYNTHETIC BIOLOGY, ACCORDING TO ONE of its definitions, is a movement to make biology easier to engineer. Synthetic biology is also a hardware and software movement. Among the hardware makers is Bento Bio, maker of the Bento Lab, a laptop-sized DNA laboratory. The lab comes with a thermocycler to run the polymerase chain reaction, a centrifuge, and a gel electrophoresis box to separate DNA and proteins.[34] Bento Lab plays into the open-source hardware Arduino and Raspberry Pi movements that empower citizens to co-create and be technology literate. What makes Bento different is that the company is creating open, inexpensive hardware powered by easy-to-use software to give makers, students, artists, and scientists access to the tools that make molecular biology possible. Bethan Wolfenden, one of the original founders, is a veteran of the International Genetically Engineered Machine (iGEM) competition and a synthetic biology doctoral student in London.

JOHN CUMBERS: What was the inspiration for Bento?

BETHAN WOLFENDEN: Bento started as an iGEM project. In 2012, my co-founder, Philip Boeing, and I had joined an iGEM team and were collaborating with London Biohackspace. There, we realized you could do molecular biology outside the academic setting.

We thought that synthetic biology was an incredible tool and didn't want to wait until we finished our Ph.D.s to stay involved with the do-it-yourself bio community. We figured that if you wanted to reach a larger audience and expand the community, you needed infrastructure. You needed something tangible that people could hold in their hand.

Our original plan was to create projects that we were interested in doing. Projects that were connected to synthetic biology but also to the general DIY bio community. To do that, we learned you needed equipment that was affordable and user-friendly. Equipment that you use intuitively.

We asked ourselves, "If I'm going to do synthetic biology, what do I need to get started?"

The answer was, you need hardware, you need reagents, and you also need knowledge.

The hardware is expensive. You can get the reagents if you're creative enough. As for knowledge, you can look at protocols but they're not well documented. If you start by reading someone's published experiment, you quickly learn it's not like reading a recipe book. They're always at a high level, you have to decode them. Good luck with that.

We envisioned this ecosystem where the hardware would be easily accessible, you could get the reagents, and find easy-to-understand, easy-to-share protocols.

KARL SCHMIEDER: It seems perfect for the do-it-yourself biotech movement. Were you inspired by the open-source software movement?

BETHAN WOLFENDEN: One of the things you end up seeing a lot in the DIY bio community and iGEM is people recreating elements of a project that someone has already done. People use BioBricks, they add components, or they add new ones, but there is a lot of repetition.

We created Bento in response to that. We wanted to offer everything you needed to get started, but also wanted to make sure that you could hold the device in your hand. We wanted to guide you with protocols so you wouldn't get discouraged. That kind of thinking was informed by open-source and software development.

We started building prototypes for inspiration and showed them to people. We asked what they wanted. We were getting invited to science fairs. That allowed us to speak to a lot of different people in different markets. We got feedback. We ended up speaking to hundreds of people and integrated that feedback into our process. Now that we understand the process, we realize that was early customer discovery.

At a certain point, they started to ask, "How do we get this? Can we buy this from you?" That's when we realized we might have a business and were ready to create the product.

JOHN CUMBERS: What has been the reaction to the product?

BETHAN WOLFENDEN: We launched in April of 2016 and sold 300 units of our first product, the Bento Lab. The starter kit is the second. In February 2017, we launched an online learning platform geared toward beginners. Our goal is to transition from hardware to helping users use the hardware.

It's been interesting to see the unique applications being developed by the user base. The Bento Lab fits into traditional businesses such as agriculture. People in agriculture have asked us if they could use the Lab to collect molecular data. They see it as a low-cost way to collect the data in the field. We expect it will be good enough for their purposes.

Another example is microbreweries. They typically send samples to labs to test for contaminants, for example microbes that could be found with a PCR test. With Bento, they can do that in-house and get a result in two or three hours. As a result, they don't have to outsource and can do it in-house on a daily basis. We expect it will be suitable for their purposes.

More recently, we got an unusual inquiry from a textile restorer. They wanted to use DNA analysis to identify the fibers in textiles in a museum exhibit. That's not something we would have thought of as an application.

Since we work alongside an architecture firm, we've learned they often have to test for anthrax because many of the old buildings in London have walls made of lath and plaster that used horsehair. There have been cases where anthrax has been found in London because of this, so we could see some applications around testing in buildings.

We're looking forward to seeing how the community ends up using the labs, develops the protocols, and helps us move the company forward.

DAN WIDMAIER: BREWING SUSTAINABLE MATERIALS TODAY

BOLT THREADS CREATES SILK PROTEINS using a fermentation process, much like brewing beer, and spins the raw proteins into fibers. In 2016, the eco-conscious outdoor brand Patagonia signed a deal with the San Francisco-based startup to develop goods made from its proprietary spider silk-inspired fibers and textiles. In early 2017, the company debuted its first product—a tie made from spider silk proteins. In July 2017, the company announced a collaboration with the luxury lifestyle brand, Stella McCartney. Dan Widmaier, Ph.D., is Bolt Thread's founder and Chief Executive Officer. Before founding the company, he conducted research on genetic circuit design to control microbial organelles. Below are Dan's responses to questions we emailed him.

Describe Bolt Threads origin story. How has the company changed since you founded it?

DAN WIDMAIER: Bolt Threads was founded on the idea that 1.5 billion years of evolution on our planet has created materials that combine high performance characteristics with environmental compatibility. The challenge is that evolution doesn't tune for modern production, economics, or availability.

We saw an opportunity to use biotechnology to bring these amazing materials to the marketplace at high quality, mass quantities, and affordable prices. This remains our vision today.

What's the future vision for Bolt Threads? How has your strategy changed over the life of the company?

DAN WIDMAIER: The improvement of materials and the capabilities available to us as designers tells the story of modern civilization.

Before we had rubber, you couldn't imagine making a better wheel with a tire. Before high modulus steel, you couldn't imagine building skyscrapers. Before the lithium ion polymer battery, you couldn't imagine making a Tesla.

We have exhausted the low-hanging fruit for innovating from petroleum feedstocks. A much more diverse set of feature spaces are available in protein polymers. We are bringing this to consumers in the form of visible material technologies in products you can buy. We believe we are igniting a new revolution in what is possible.

How is the biological manufacturing of materials a net positive for the environment?

DAN WIDMAIER: We use a lot of materials in our modern consumer society. For better or worse, the norm is to create and use disposable products.

In the last century, the chemicals industry created wonderful world-changing plastic products. Now, though, we're seeing the emergence of long-term problems because of the disconnect between the resource intensity necessary to create those products and the life cycle expectations of consumer society.

Making consumer products from the materials that nature creates makes them inherently biocompatible. It leads to a baseline economy where everything can be recycled by the existing cycles in the biosphere—the carbon, nitrogen, and water cycles.

Are we entering a new age for bio-engineered fabrics? What does the future look like?

DAN WIDMAIER: Technically, we're on the cusp of a new age of bio-engineered fabrics. The major hurdle remaining is matching the scale of the technology with the size of the opportunity. This has proven quite challenging for biomanufacturing. It can and will be done, it's just a matter of when.

After seven years, the one thing I've learned is I can't predict the future precisely, but I can say that amazing things do happen and will come to market. Serendipity is always astounding when developing a new technology.

What fabric do you wish existed that does not yet?

DAN WIDMAIER: I want a fabric that can change color like a chameleon to match your environment and stay that color until you switch it, but without needing electricity.

ANDRAS FORGACS: DESIGN AND BIOFABRICATION IS REVOLUTIONIZING MATERIALS

WHEN YOU LOOK AT THE synthetic biology community, there are companies manufacturing genes, developing computational tools, and creating cloud labs and automation tools. Others are engineering organisms and developing applications using living materials. The definition includes companies that use biology to fabricate things—biofabrication companies.

Brooklyn-based Modern Meadow grew out of the ground-breaking tissue and organ printing company, Organovo. Some of the tools developed at Organovo were originally used by the company to create meat and leather. As the company progressed, its focus became leather materials. Andras Forgacs is the founder and CEO.

KARL SCHMIEDER: How do you summarize what Modern Meadow does?

ANDRAS FORGACS: We combine innovations at different scales—both the subcellular and macroscopic levels.

Many synthetic biology companies are focused on creating small molecules, proteins, or enzymes by using tools that work at a subcellular level. That is a substantial component of our product but that's only part of the process. We also work at the macroscopic level, organizing collagen proteins so we can create new leather materials with a higher order structure than what is available from animals.

JOHN CUMBERS: You were one of the co-founders of Organovo—that was also a biofabrication company. Why didn't Organovo focus on creating materials?

ANDRAS FORGACS: Organovo pioneered tissue engineering, a specific type of biofabrication that uses mammalian cells to create higher order structures. The company didn't work at the subcellular level. It does not focus on genetically modifying cells and does not combine cell engineering with the tissue engineering. Making different materials would be out of scope for Organovo.

KARL SCHMIEDER: Explain how your Organovo experience led to starting Modern Meadow?

ANDRAS FORGACS: Two things happened. First, people who knew the company started asking if we could do other things with the biofabrication technology. They asked, "If you can print skin in three dimensions, could you make muscle and use it to test drugs? If you can biofabricate skin, can you produce hide for leather? If you can print muscle, could you make meat?" Again, those projects were out of scope for Organovo, but the questions were intriguing.

Second, I went to China where I saw how animal products—either worn or consumed—were a gigantic industry dependent on multiple externalities. Animal products grew more expensive every year I was in China. Quality issues were abundant and the environmental impact was significant. I started to wonder if Organovo's technologies had broader applications beyond medicine.

Large leather buyers familiar with my work at Organovo were calling and asking, "If you can grow skin, can't you make leather?" That was out of scope for Organovo but when you're an entrepreneur and you get enough of those calls, you start to think there is a new business to form and you figure it out.

It so happens a few of the scientists who had developed the technology were available to work on other projects. My experience is that a new company or new idea typically comes from a combination of three things: technology, team, and opportunity. It's usually one of those that starts the process and begins the virtuous cycle of getting the others.

In this case, we had an insight on a technology, we had an exceptional team, and we were being given an exceptional opportunity. We applied for and received Small Business Innovation Research funding from the U.S. Department of Agriculture and the National Science Foundation. We got early-stage funding from Breakout Labs, then got involved with Singularity University. We continued to refine the technology, expanded the team with different capabilities, and have arrived at the biofabrication process we are using today.

JOHN CUMBERS: You pivoted away from producing food. How has the company and the technology changed?

ANDRAS FORGACS: At the beginning we were focused on both creating food and materials. Of course, the press loves the most sensational part of the story, so if you're focused on producing food and materials, they're going to focus on food because that gets the most reactions.

What we did at the beginning was based on my previous experiences with biology and bio-entrepreneurship. We focused on integrating cell engineering and tissue engineering to create meat and leather. As we iterated, we realized the opportunity for leather materials was significant enough and an exciting challenge on its own, so we made that the focus of Modern Meadow.

What we're doing now is very different from when we started. We're no longer as literal about tissue engineering. That's why we say we are a biofabrication company. We use biology on the front end and combine it with several other disciplines—biological engineering, material science, chemistry, and process design. All of those disciplines work at different scales, on different levels.

Our entire focus as a company is to create the right structure of the collagen that makes up the leather. We've evolved the technology to produce the collagen in a way that is economically scalable and creates the highest quality material.

Our technology is getting better every day. We have more control over the performance properties of our materials and the aesthetics are better. In addition, by focusing on large-scale biofabrication, we are improving the economics of scale.

KARL SCHMIEDER: Biofabrication is a relatively new idea. How does it impact supply chains and the environment?

ANDRAS FORGACS: The livestock industry is very resource intensive. It requires huge amounts of land. It consumes water and food. It's one of the biggest contributors to greenhouse gas emissions.

I was highly motivated to create a product that could be used every day, that everybody could relate to, and that could make a dent in the way we use our planet's resources. The fact that we can impact animal welfare and the environment is important to me. We're helping create a cleaner supply chain and deliver materials that do not require as much chemical processing.

KARL SCHMIEDER: How do you think biotechnology impacts consumers every day?

ANDRAS FORGACS: Consumer awareness of biotechnology is low but that's changing. Biology is becoming part of a brand's story. You're already seeing this with companies like Impossible Foods and the spider silk companies Bolt Threads, Amsilk and Spiber.

What's interesting is biotechnology itself has the potential to be the headline, an important headline, because it can deliver important benefits to the product and consumers. Biology has the ability to create product attributes that are not possible using conventional manufacturing methods. Biofabrication also offers environmental benefits. That's a differentiator that can be an important part of the brand story.

Remember, consumers aren't just buying products for what they are. Certainly, that's an important part of the purchase decision. But consumers are also buying products based on how they are made, the story behind them, and the experience associated with a brand.

Over the next several years, companies are going to offer products where the story is the virtue—biofabrication—as well as the characteristics created through biology. That will be an important part of the brand. That is totally new. In the consumer space, biology has the potential to be a game changer.

EBEN BAYER: CHICKENS ARE MORE COMPLICATED THAN IPHONES

EBEN BAYER, CO-FOUNDER AND CEO of Ecovative, is a leader in the biomaterials industry. He is a co-inventor of Mycobond, strong, natural building composites created by growing organisms that turn low-value agricultural waste products into strong natural composites. With Ecovative, he is leading efforts to create sustainable and affordable products.

JOHN CUMBERS: What is Ecovative's origin story?

EBEN BAYER: It started as a university project. A very influential professor asked us to work on solving really big problems. I had this insight about mycelium. We've used it as food for hundreds, thousands of years. Then, I started asking, "What if we looked at this organism—not as a food source—but as a material?"

Once you analyze mycelium through the lens of material science, you realize it's like living glue, like living plastic. The filamentous strands of mycelium are a nano-bot.

We started Ecovative in 2007. The first three years were focused on research and development, creating a minimal viable product, and trying to figure out what mycelium does best. We thought we were going to launch with building insulation—which we do manufacture today—but when push came to shove, we realized that was a challenging proof of concept. We pivoted and created a packaging product to replace styrofoam. That change of focus allowed us to do small boutique [manufacturing] runs and acquire customers. Because of that first product, we were able to team up with Sealed Air to offer our first product across America.

In 2016, we produced more than 1 million pounds of MycoFoam to replace plastic packaging for companies like Toyota, Dell, IBM, and others. Realistically, that's a lot of product for us to manufacture, but in terms of impact, it's only a fraction of a percent of U.S. styrofoam.

The raw materials don't drive the price. In fact, our raw material is quite competitive with oil-based styrene in an amorphous form. The additional cost is growing the materials, creating the molds, and working at scale with automation. We've taken it to a level that lets us price at the higher end of the market, which is typically using heavier, denser foams. We compete at price parity in that market segment.

The challenge is that the bulk of the market is extremely low density, low quality foams. From a technical point of view, there is no reason why you can't compete in that segment on price. However, our business strategy is to move up the cost-curve into durable goods and higher value products.

KARL SCHMIEDER: Even though you say it's only a fraction of a percent of U.S. styrofoam, can you calculate the environmental benefit?

EBEN BAYER: We've done the carbon footprint analysis in the past and it's tricky. It depends on what you're doing with the product. For example, if you incinerate polystyrene, your carbon footprint is much higher than if you put it into a landfill.

In all scenarios, our products net out positively. My focus with that product is the stuff that ends up in the ocean. It's predicted that by 2030 there will be more plastic in the ocean than fish. If our product ends up in the ocean, it's fish food. That is the common good we're going after. It's not only about the carbon dioxide, it's about toxicity reduction for the planet.

JOHN CUMBERS: What's your long-term vision for Ecovative?

EBEN BAYER: What makes us special is that we use biofabrication. We use the whole organism to create materials. Our longer term vision is the use of fungal cells to grow a whole range of materials with varying properties from low-density plastic foams that behave like styrofoam, to thermoset resins that behave like glue and are used in engineered wood to make particle board.

JOHN CUMBERS: You don't currently use any genetically modified organisms (GMOs) in your products, but you're pro-GMO. Could you explain?

EBEN BAYER: For the record, I am very much pro-GMO. The ability to control biology, especially in higher-level organisms, especially like the ones we're working with, will change the world the way the personal computer did.

We're at an inflection point. At Ecovative, we work with native strains [of mycelium] that just work. Now, we're in a program with DARPA to create a GMO bug that we have complete control over. That will transform what we do because as you gain control over that system, you have a programmable living plastic, a programmable polymer. To me, that is super exciting because we're working with an optimized native platform that competes with synthetics today and we're moving toward one we can optimize and tailor to specific applications.

Think about it. The chemical industry has been optimizing plastic chemistry for half a century. Once we get the toolkit that allows us to program mycelium's biology, we'll compete with plastics in ways we are not able to today.

I know people are scared of GMOs but that's because of the way they were introduced to society. You can use the tool for good or bad. People are sensitive about what they put in their bodies. That's where GMOs show up—in food. The way they showed up in food wasn't aspirational. People didn't say, "We're going to make rice with the extra amino acids you need." Instead, it was more like, "Let's make the crops that can tolerate herbicides. Crops that could tolerate more pesticides." If the first GMOs showed up in consumer furniture, people would be less freaked out by the technology.

When I go to a conference like GreenBuild,[35] there is a lot of environmental consciousness, I get a lot of friction on the GMO point. People will ask, "Are there GMOs in your product?"

I'll answer, "No, but I wish there were." You should see people who are in love with you. Their faces drop.

KARL SCHMIEDER: Could you give us more details on the DARPA project?

EBEN BAYER: Sure, we're focused on two exciting projects. First, we're engineering microbial communities to gain control of the fungi we use. Most folks in biotechnology grow on liquid media. We grow on solid culture. When we studied our solid culture, we learned we're using a combination of fungi and bacteria. We started to look at how we can create an industrial microbiome of our solid culture and control the gene expression between cultures.

You can gain control of the fungi by modifying cell wall chemistry and/or by metabolic engineering to improve how it grows. You can also change the branching dynamics since physically, the fungi builds microstructures that are signaling pathways that tell it how frequently to branch. That branching has an impact on how tough the material is. [The ability to engineer the fungi] moves us out of the realm of process control and into the realm of [controlling] the characteristics of the organism.

The second thing we're doing with DARPA is a bit crazier. We're using living materials to create buildings. The idea is that if a soldier were injured in the field, you could add water and the building would assemble itself as a structure [to provide protection].

JOHN CUMBERS: What near-term impacts do you think we'll see around biotechnology?

EBEN BAYER: I think the biggest change will be when living objects with biological functions leave the bioreactor and become desktop devices in consumer products.

I envision a future where you have living biological products either as the structure you live in or as items you put in your pocket. We're close to engineering things in your home like a smoke detector using living cellular systems. In that case, the product is a living system and its functions come not from a silicon chip but from bacteria or fungi that are alive and responding to their environment.

When we're able to use living organisms as consumer devices, you'll have the incredible richness of the technological complexity that has made our world so great, but without the cost to the environment. Living devices will help us replace the extractable resources, the heavy metals, the constant stream of consumer crap that ends up in landfills. We can replicate all of that technology using biology, keeping living cells that are alive in consumer objects. Then you completely eliminate the environmental costs and it would be no different than throwing an apple on the ground or composting [the remains of] a chicken. Chickens are way more complicated than iPhones and they provide a net benefit. They provide nutrients and synthesize another chicken.

Biomaterials like those Ecovative produces are going to impact slow-moving industries like construction, architecture, interiors. We're working with a wood furniture company that has been around for 100 years. Their bio strategy has been trees. But when we go from biomaterials to living materials, where cells have been engineered to deliver functionality, everything changes. It will blow the doors open on all industries. Everything then will be consumer product, consumer-driven.

JOHN MELO: INDUSTRIAL BIOTECHNOLOGY CONFERS THE STRONGEST COMPETITIVE ADVANTAGE

JOHN G. MELO SERVES AS the chief executive officer of Amyris Biotechnologies. He is a thought leader in the global fuels industry and technology innovation. At Amyris, he's been focused on reducing the cost of curing malaria and producing lower carbon, second-generation biofuels. One of the first synthetic biology companies, Amyris provides sustainable alternatives to a broad range of petroleum-sourced products and rare materials.

JOHN CUMBERS: In the past, you have said the hardest thing for Amryis wasn't the technology, but helping businesses understand why they should adopt biotechnology. Could you explain?

JOHN MELO: Let me clarify. The most significant investments that we have made as a company have been in technology and manufacturing. However, getting customer adoption and customer acceptance of our final products has been even more challenging. In that regard, our efforts have focused on developing strong partnerships that both define technology/product target, and provide channels to market in ways that yield an adoption cycle or acceptance process for our products.

JOHN CUMBERS: Are you saying producing a great product and being cost-competitive aren't good enough?

JOHN MELO: Exactly. The markets for our products are amazing, but we've seen great technologies that never went anywhere. Not because the product wasn't excellent but because the customers didn't really like it for whatever reason.

JOHN CUMBERS: You started your career in the petroleum industry, could you contrast that with the biotechnology industry?

JOHN MELO: Let me take a technical perspective. The geology and the topography of the world has been mapped and is fairly well understood in terms of natural resources. The oil industry is about CAPEX—capital expenses—to explore, build platforms, and produce oil and gas. Oil fields have been discovered. The products being created are well understood. Markets are well defined.

When I look at biology and the pathways in organisms, they're not well understood. In contrast, biology is all about OPEX—operating expenses—to develop a strain, energy requirements to operate that strain in a big tank, and end-product and its value.

Biology is still about exploration. The market for bio-manufactured, bio-based products is not well defined.

JOHN CUMBERS: You made a significant investment in developing bio-fuels, but there hasn't been as much interest of late—what does the future look like for bio-based fuels?

JOHN MELO: There was a lot of hype and excitement around bio-fuels in the mid-2000s. That's because there was a lot of published information that lead to an understanding that we were moving into a world of constrained natural resources. In other words, a world of scarcity.

Over the next ten years—around 2010, 2011, 2012—we transitioned to a world of abundance. In that three-year period, we saw a shift in trends and demand. A revolution took place with shale, solar, and other renewable energy technologies. It dramatically shifted the outlook for renewable fuels.

When I talk about renewable fuels, I mean liquid fuels. When you look at the world of the next 100 years as a world of abundance, the level of capital available to develop and produce new bio-fuels technologies is dramatically lower. Especially when you compare it to the late-1990s, early-2000s.

JOHN CUMBERS: Does that mean the tax incentives to produce bio-fuels are dead in the water?

JOHN MELO: I think at this point we get that feeling, but scarcity and abundance are deeply important. I understand there is a climate issue but if you really believe the world has abundance going forward, the better way to address the issue is to focus on consumer habits. You move the production of electricity to renewable sources. It's not [let's] take tax dollars to develop new bio-fuels.

JOHN CUMBERS: What about the idea of taxing CO_2 emissions or the environmental damage they do, would that tip the balance against using them?

JOHN MELO: Oil is subsidizing a lot of places around the world that produce oil. The problem is that in many of those places, governments that don't want to give up their power base. As a result, a third of the price of a barrel of oil is going into the pockets of the consumers in those areas to keep them happy. You can't get to sustainable next generation renewable fuels on economics that would require subsidies equal to the price of an automobile today.

Today, the actual value of a gallon of fuel is less than a dollar and it's going to stay there for a long time to come. Believe me, I'm a huge fan of renewable bio-fuels. I was hoping and still hope we will continue to do the best we can to create and sell renewable jet fuels. Do I believe that industrial biotechnology will be underpinned by an amazing play in renewable bio-fuels? I don't think so.

JOHN CUMBERS: What do non-biotech businesses need to know about what's happening with biology and biotechnology?

JOHN MELO: Industrial biotech is violently disruptive. It confers the strongest competitive advantage that any company can gain.

Bio-based products deliver an alternative supply source without the volatility at a much lower price and with better performance. When a company develops a product or uses ingredients that are manufactured biologically, they will absolutely disrupt their markets. We're seeing that play out across our entire customer-base.

JOHN CUMBERS: Could you let us know the types of conversations you have with non-biotech customers?

JOHN MELO: Sure. Let me first let you know what's typically in the minds of the CEOs that I engage with. They are thinking a few things. One is, "Yes. Biology. It sounds like a science experiment." They won't say it, but you can often tell it's on their minds. They don't see it as a real business.

The second thing we hear, and it's amazing, is, "We've been investing $10 million, $20 million, even $100 million a year on biotechnology and we still haven't seen any tangible products. I'm not sure I want to keep doing this."

The third is my favorite. This is where companies say, "We've heard this before. We engaged a project with X company. They met all their milestones, but they couldn't scale. It was a nightmare project, and we don't want to do that anymore."

Our success has been to break all that apart and get back to the basics. At the end of the day, you have to develop a product that makes you money and changes your business. If I can't demonstrate that for you, then you shouldn't pay. If it's not a business, we don't want you to do it. It has to be a real business. A business that works. It should be better than most of the investments they make internally.

In terms of the second part, we talk to companies that made internal investments but didn't see the product. Often, they never really invested enough or brought in enough technology to industrialize the science. They really are doing science experiments internally then blaming the technology for not working. We end up spending a lot of time with our partners solving these problems.

JOHN CUMBERS: At that point, how do you get them to reconsider biology as a solution?

JOHN MELO: I really want them to look at their product portfolio and all the ingredients they use and the products they make. I want to know which ingredients have big swings in price quarter on quarter, or year on year. Finally, I want them to look at any ingredient that costs more than three dollars per kilo, ingredients that they're losing market share because a competitor has developed a better feature, increased production, or improved the offer to the end customer.

When we understand those three areas, we can often demonstrate how biotechnology can provide a better solution for them. By the way, with those three criteria, I have rarely seen a business that won't benefit from a biological solution.

SECTION 3. BIOLOGICAL ESCAPE VELOCITY

BIOLOGY IS IN TRANSITION.

Our understanding of biology has advanced over the past 40 years. In many ways, the modern biotechnology industry is more art than engineering discipline. We've witnessed a decrease in the price of reading and writing DNA.

That said, in many ways, biotechnology as art is slow. It currently takes two weeks to go through a design-build-test cycle. Moving from concept to final product takes too long.

We are moving quickly toward having the ability to design a metabolic pathway or organism on a computer, print the DNA with a DNA printer, then test the resulting organism within a few hours.

We call the measurement of this cycle, "biological escape velocity." When biological escape velocity reaches real-time, biotechnology will become a true engineering discipline.

At that moment, our understanding of biology will advance at the limits of human creativity.

We expect that biology will become a true engineering discipline. A Cambrian explosion of innovation will take place. It will disrupt many existing industries and create new ones. It is the next major technology.

In this section, you'll read interviews with visionaries imagining the future of engineered biology and entrepreneurs creating the microbial design industry. You'll also read about synthetic biology's societal impacts, and the need to engage the public as the technologies progress and become commercialized.

JAY KEASLING: PREPARE FOR THE BIOLOGICAL IPHONE

JAY D. KEASLING, PH.D., IS considered one of the foremost authorities in synthetic biology, especially in the field of metabolic engineering. He's a professor of chemical engineering and bioengineering at the University of California, Berkeley. His lab engineered both *E. coli* and *Saccharomyces cerevisiae* to produce a precursor to artemisinin to treat malaria. Dr. Keasling also runs Lawrence Berkeley National Laboratory and is chief executive officer at the Joint BioEnergy Institute.

JOHN CUMBERS: About ten years ago, you set out on a mission to make biology easier to engineer, how do you think we are doing?

JAY KEASLING: We're doing better than we were. Around 2006 biology was much more challenging to engineer. If we look at the decade before that, it was even more challenging. It has definitely gotten easier.

I think we've seen the progress because we've created organizations like Synberc[36] that bring people together. We've built a community to get people to share ideas and tools they're creating. We've gotten people on a common platform. There's a common understanding. All of that has contributed.

JOHN CUMBERS: Where does that work need to go to further commercialize biology? To integrate it into our daily lives?

JAY KEASLING: The biggest challenge with biology is we're engineering life. It can get out of control. That's a real possibility—especially as we make is easier to engineer. But there are a couple of things.

First, biology is still difficult to engineer, so developing applications and platforms takes a lot of time and money. We're a long way from where we need to be. While that frustrates some of us, it's actually OK. The public isn't ready for biology to be as easy as buying an iPhone, iPad, or any consumer electronics device where you can create and deploy apps.

Second, you just can't turn biology on then throw it away. If an app on my iPhone or iPad doesn't work, I can delete it. If my iPhone doesn't work, I can get a new one. It's not that easy with life. There are implications that we need to think through.

Let's say you buy and boot up a [genetically engineered or cloned] pet on a regular basis, can you just throw it away when you upgrade? Probably not. When we engineer life to produce chemicals, we have to worry about the release of microbes. There are the safety concerns.

While I would like it to be much easier to engineer, I don't think the public is ready. We have as much work to do on the public side as we do on the engineering side.

KARL SCHMIEDER: Where do you think we should put our energy in terms of the public debate around biosecurity?

JAY KEASLING: I'm extremely biased. My opinion is based on my own experience. I've focused on engineering microbes and they have a lot of attractive features. They're in tanks, so you can control them, manipulate them, and dispose of them. Enabling applications around microbes in tanks is great because there is so much that can be done with them.

Maybe the public feels OK about microbes when they are in tanks, controlled, and being used for business-to-business application. For the time being, there aren't any person-to-person applications, though that will quickly change with your own private microbiome.

As we get to things like plants, insects, and animals we have to start talking about something different. We have to consider the environment. There's less control outside the tank.

From my perspective, working on applications around microbes and maybe plants and energy is OK. Beyond that, we have a lot of work to do with the public. If they don't see these things changing their lives for the better, they're going to have a hard time with engineered biology.

KARL SCHMIEDER: Do you have any ideas how we should improve engagement with the public around biotechnology?

JAY KEASLING: We have been doing it and need to continue. We have to be very proactive about this because there is a group of people that will be incredibly reactive and will scare the public.

I lived through this. We engineered yeast to produce artemisinin as an antimalarial drug for poor children in Africa. I thought I had this perfect application for helping the poor in Africa, engineering microbes in tanks, producing a drug that is in limited supply and is too expensive for them. But the people who are very anti-GMO, anti-technology, still came out against it. They came out in force against me.

I think we did an OK job handling it but if they can be against that then it will be very easy for them be against fuel and products that are aimed at the affluent.

KARL SCHMIEDER: When you think about the tools and technologies we have available, what's missing right now? What would make your work easier?

JAY KEASLING: We should be able to boot up a bacterial cell at will, de novo. I know Craig Venter has done that with the minimal cell. Jef Boeke's doing it with the yeast chromosome.[37] But I'm talking about a microbial cell. If we had a bootable microbial cell, we would have a much better understanding of how every gene works and how every protein interacts in the cell. We would understand which proteins are necessary, which aren't. I could go on and on but it would be an incredible driver of technology and development. If I were working on the next generation of Synberc, I would focus on booting up a microbial cell.

JOHN CUMBERS: We're in a funding cycle for synthetic biology, with more than $1 billion invested in 2016 and the CRISPR IPOs.[38] You've been through a number of these cycles, in particular the biofuels boom in 2008 to 2009. Could you reflect on that?

JAY KEASLING: Funding goes in cycles. It always has. I came into Codon Devices late.[39] It was already off the ground when they asked me to join. Amyris was one of the biggest synthetic biology plays at the time, but it came in during the cleantech boom.

Today, I think the difference with synthetic biology is we're not on the cleantech side. It's almost the opposite. The investments in cleantech resembled the biotech industry in that you had to be a late-stage company to get funding. Twenty years ago, you had people who were funding [biotechnology enabling] platforms. Then they said, "We're not funding platforms any more. We want to fund applications." That happened on the cleantech side. Now people again are willing to fund platforms in synthetic biology, but it's harder to fund applications.

I'd like there to be knowledgeable investors putting lots of money in these things. I don't think that's always the case and I worry it disempowers the community. I'd prefer to have knowledgeable investors who know the field, want to grow the field and can be patient. That way the busts wouldn't be as low and the booms wouldn't be as high.

DREW ENDY: THE COMMERCIAL OPPORTUNITIES FOR BIOTECHNOLOGY ARE INFINITE

DREW ENDY, Ph.D., is one of the leaders of synthetic biology. He's been called "an engineer's biologist" since he likes to create new tools for building organisms that "do stuff." Dr. Endy was one of the founders of the International Genetic Engineered Machine Competition[40] (iGEM) and the BioBricks Foundation[41], a registry for standard biological parts. He teaches at Stanford University and recently started bionet.io,[42] an open technology foundation to enable the scalable peer-to-peer exchange and tracking of materials used throughout biomedical research.

KARL SCHMIEDER: In 2005, you published a *Nature* paper titled "Foundations for Engineering Biology,"[43] can you give us some background on how that paper came to be?

DREW ENDY: In 1999, I was a fellow at the Molecular Sciences Institute[44] in Berkeley. I started saying things like, "We need to rebuild the living world so that it becomes model-able." But the only person who responded was Tom Knight at the Massachusetts Institute of Technology. He said, "Of course. That code is four billion years old. It's time for a rewrite."

Tom made many simple and elegant observations about biology. Through him I learned that if I wanted to conduct an experiment with genes, I needed to do two experiments. The first is building the DNA [or the genes] that I need. The second, is the experiment I care about. I'd rather not have to do that first experiment. Tom taught me the toolkit for practicing biotechnology sucks.

Fast-forward to 2003. For 18 months, I chaired a committee of 50 scientists assembled by the Defense Advanced Research Projects

Agency (DARPA) to determine the best ways to advance the engineering of biology. The briefing[45] we gave DARPA would become the *Nature* paper, Foundations for Engineering Biology.[46] We had three ideas.

First, separate design from manufacturing or fabrication. In biotechnology, this means separating DNA synthesis from end-product design. My metaphor is to separate the architects from the general contractors.

Second, coordinate labor via standards. Standards underlie most aspects of the modern world. Railroad gauges, screw threads, internet addresses, rebar for reinforcing concrete, gasoline formulations, units of measure, and so much more are standardized.

Third, manage the complexity of biology by adapting abstraction ideas from computer science. Without programming languages, coders would need to learn to work in ones and zeros, or machine language, to communicate directly with a central processing unit or any computer hardware. Without a programming language, synthetic biologists would always need to work at the level of DNA's four nucleotides, adenine, cytosine, guanine, and thymine. Our idea was write high-level code, compile it, and make the design and testing of new biological systems easier.

JOHN CUMBERS: Could you describe the progress the field has made on those three items over the course of the past 12 years?

DREW ENDY: First, separating design from manufacturing or fabrication. In 2003, the price of gene synthesis was $4 a base pair. That was discounted because John Mulligan, who ran Blue Heron,[47] gave us that price. I remember ordering 20,000 base pairs for $80,000 and being thrilled.

From 2003 to 2016, we've seen a hundred-fold decrease in the cost of writing DNA. Today, if you have a big contract for DNA synthesis, you can pay as little as a penny a base pair. As a result, you're seeing companies that are designers or testers of ideas then outsource the construction. This is like Apple doing all the design work on the iPhone and having a company like Foxconn manufacture it. Ginkgo BioWorks is the best known example but there are many others.

Second, coordinating labor via standards. That was misunderstood and controversial in the research community. There was no such thing as a standard biological part in 2003. The idea that you could put a sequence into a computer, type it out, and get something that behaves as expected was a fantasy. Scientists said we could never create reliable, reusable, composable biological parts. Today, BioBricks, the registry for standard biological parts, has more than 20,000 parts characterized and it's growing every year.

The challenge is there is no market for standardized biological parts. People don't know what to do with BioBricks. Plus, individuals and companies can solve so many low-hanging fruit problems without them. In other words, you don't need standards or coordination of labor in biotechnology to solve significant problems.

KARL SCHMIEDER: Could you give us an example of a low-hanging fruit project?

DREW ENDY: Sure. Last year, my wife, Christina Smolke, and her team at Stanford, figured out how to brew opiates from yeast.[48] That required composing a pathway of 30 enzymes. They spun out a company, Antheia Bio,[49] with a team of less than ten people. They don't need to coordinate labor or workflow with anyone but can reach annual markets approaching US$3 billion to US$5 billion per year.

Richard Kitney of the Imperial College of London likes to use the example of automobile manufacturing. He says BMW coordinates hundreds, if not thousands, of suppliers to make their cars. That requires massive coordination and standards.

What is synthetic biology's equivalent of a four-door sedan? There isn't one yet.

When we start engineering multi-cellular organisms then we'll need to integrate thousands of components. We can manage the complexity of biology by adapting abstraction ideas from computer science.

For example, in 2013 we published a paper in *Science* on amplifying genetic logic gates.[50] We showed that you could put several DNA switches or transcriptors in *E. coli* and build logic circuits to program a cell's behavior. What isn't clear in that paper is that we used abstraction and standards to create every logic gate. It took us less than two months to do all the work.

JOHN CUMBERS: Are there any examples of abstraction in biology being put to use today?

DREW ENDY: The rollout of CRISPR reflects how a bit of abstraction and some standards can be incredibly powerful. Abstraction simplified CRISPR, standards made it accessible.

I would say that in the decade that followed 2003 to 2013, we've driven the cost of DNA synthesis down a hundred-fold. We've shown that we can create standard biological parts, but most people don't want or need them yet. There is no market and abstraction is possible but needs to be realized for the rest of living matter.

The core ideas that I wrote about in 2003 and 2005 are solid. Some of the fundamentals have been deciphered, the groundwork completed, but there is so much more work to do. There is a massive opportunity for infrastructure investment and building that will depend as much on motivation and incentives as the actual technology.

We need another decade or so to shape the engineering landscape of biotechnology, but the commercial opportunities are infinite.

ELEONORE PAUWELS: THE INTERSECTION OF GENOMICS, SYNTHETIC BIOLOGY, ARTIFICIAL INTELLIGENCE, AND SECURITY

ELEONORE PAUWELS IS THE DIRECTOR of Science Innovation with the Science and Technology Innovation Program at the Wilson Center in Washington, D.C. She studies, writes, and speaks frequently on the intersection of genomics, synthetic biology, artificial intelligence, and intellectual property. As biological technologies become digitized, they will face the same security issues as information technologies.

KARL SCHMIEDER: Technology is changing at an exponential pace that is often hard to understand. How should governments prepare to deal with life science technologies that are so new and evolve so quickly that regulatory pathways haven't yet been defined?

ELEONOR PAUWELS: The challenge is how do we train people to anticipate the implications of new technologies.

Right now, the risk between Silicon Valley and [Washington] D.C., is the speed of entrepreneurship. Business models that worked in IT or digital are very quickly being transferred to biology. When things move as fast as they are moving, it's difficult to anticipate the implications. We're not very good at that.

Most of the time, the federal workforce is playing catch up with what is happening in Silicon Valley, the Boston corridor, and other places.

It's impossible for federal workers to understand what technologies are real or hype. It's hard to understand upstream and downstream, near-term and long-term implications. There also is the problem of having a well-trained workforce able to anticipate new technologies and their convergence.

For example, very few people understand the implications of using gene drives in a specific ecosystem, region, or neighborhood.[51] That kind of biological engineering pushes the limits of what government can do. It's especially a challenge when you don't have a workforce capable of thinking through the effects of a technology. At the same time, it's difficult to [train] technology entrepreneurs to anticipate the regulatory and workforce implications of their technologies.

KARL SCHMIEDER: Could you give an example of a technology that is misunderstood?

ELEONOR PAUWELS: Artificial Intelligence. Most of what we hear right now is about the transformative effects of AI and how it will change every industry. The truth is, we still don't really know how it's going to work.

Industry has to assess the accuracy of AI and its algorithms. Regulatory agencies face the challenge of determining the accuracy of tests and algorithms. Then, they need to figure out how to regulate the technology.

The same with CRISPR and human genome editing. The hype tells you it's easy and cheap, but when you talk to a practitioner, the story is different. I have a friend working on gene editing for sickle cell [patients]. It will take years to figure it out in the lab. It will take even longer to get it to patients. Knocking out a gene is one thing, but if you're trying to fix the immune system or repair connective tissues that will require much more work. You just can't start gene editing humans without understanding the cartography of the genome.

AI and CRISPR will impact many different systems and change the ways we operate. They will change how we deal with disease. But you need researchers and entrepreneurs speaking with the regulatory agencies to anticipate the larger implications.

KARL SCHMIEDER: Government and regulatory agencies aren't agile the way entrepreneurs must be by necessity. How does that impact the way governments work with or adapt to emerging technologies like synthetic biology?

ELEONOR PAUWELS: It takes a lot to move and reform government and regulatory systems. The system cannot properly operate on ideas or technologies that were developed 10 or 20 years ago. The machinery of government is difficult to transform and reform, because, as you say, it's not agile or adaptive.

That doesn't mean there aren't individuals or governmental departments that are adapting to cope with a new technology. There are. They are finding ways to fit technology within a specific category so that it can move forward.

At the same time, I don't see entrepreneurs thinking about the implications of their technologies beyond their direct impact. Maybe that's because entrepreneurs are driven to solve a problem and the implications are outside their thinking.

To me, the impact of AI systems analyzing our genomic data is fascinating. But whose job is it to think about that? An entrepreneur wants to get a solution to a problem, but they have no responsibility to look beyond the direct impact.

KARL SCHMIEDER: When it comes to the misuse of biotechnology, what are the things you worry about?

ELEONOR PAUWELS: I think there is still a problem around how we assess and distribute the benefits of innovations. The recent CRISPR patent battle is an example. The way that played out, a group of companies becomes less competitive because they cannot afford CRISPR. How did we conclude that only a few companies can use CRISPR and gain a competitive advantage? Instead, the technology could have become an open-source, enabling technology that would unleash innovation.

I'm concerned about the convergence of genomics and AI. It's hard to tell where the data is originating, what the protocols are for using, owning and storing the data, and what the ownership models are. Creating an ecosystem where individuals could benefit from sharing their genomics data is a lot different than one where only a few investors and companies benefit from publicly available data.

Global companies are competing to control genomics data. I worry about ownership models for an industry that is built on people's personal health data. Both scenarios signal to me that we are not moving toward an open-source, transparent model. That keeps me up at night more than what people do with biotech in a DIY lab.

KARL SCHMIEDER: Where is the intersection between cybersecurity and biotechnology?

ELEONOR PAUWELS: As more genomic data comes online it becomes vulnerable to the same data security issues. If there is a massive cyberattack on genomics data, there should be a strategy to deal with that. Would the genomics companies be responsible? The hospitals? The individuals?

I think people would panic because we really don't understand what a wide-scale cyberattack would look like, especially if all of our medical data were exposed.

We didn't anticipate how quickly China would become a powerhouse in the personalized medicine space, nor how much they are investing in both genomics and AI. We need more people thinking about this and the converging dynamics of genomics and AI.

KARL SCHMIEDER: Will we need to think about biosecurity in the same way we think about cybersecurity?

ELEONOR PAUWELS: Cybersecurity is going mainstream as an enabling technology because data is part of everything we do. We need to help people understand the information technology systems we're using, where weaknesses exist, and how checkpoints should be incorporated into the system. Biology is moving in the same direction as IT. Genomics data will face the same data security challenges as IT.

It's easy to imagine biotech tools becoming enabling technologies the same way systems did in IT. Imagine if CRISPR were distributed and democratized. If bioinformatics were distributed and democratized, you could store your data anywhere, you could exchange it, and you could create new benefits.

The analogies between the two fields are interesting but it becomes even more interesting when you start using DNA to store data. Large parts of society are not ready for this. Some people will understand the value of cybersecurity, genomics and AI. They will know how to derive value in different ways. The problem is you can still have weak points that could be entries for attacks. Threats can come from anywhere.

I recently worked on a disruptive cybersecurity project and learned we are not prepared. We must continue learning and admit we're not prepared. By the time we wake up to the possibilities and have a strategy or framework, technology will have moved on.

Imagine the Internet of Things (IoT) becomes the Bio Internet of Things. To take it a step further, you're using living sensors and storing data with DNA. You use genomic sequencing for tracking and biology becomes pervasive in the way the IOT is predicted to be. How do you organize a governance system for that?

KARL SCHMIEDER: Do you think we're making progress in terms of democratizing the tools of biotechnology?

ELEONOR PAUWELS: It's a good question. I see a lot of benefits upfront. Imagine using the Nanopore portable DNA sequencer.[52] You could track the evolution of viruses in people. You could track the evolution of biosensing in different species. You could assess pollution in different places.

The same thing happened with 3D printers. At the beginning, they were used by a small population of people in a very specific way. As soon as they were distributed, people started to use them to do different things. They are creating new materials and inventing completely new ways of using those. It's the process of design in engineering, generative design. It changes as more people enter the space.

Could that happen with bio? It's hard to imagine the things we will create as more people are able to use the tools of biotechnology.

You could argue for the downsides, the misuse of biotechnology. But I think people will create more benefits first. The people of the world want to make it a better place. They're going to develop different types of bio-sensors to track epidemics. We're not good at anticipating either the good or the threats but I think we'll see benefits first.

JOSHUA HOFFMAN: THE RELIABLE OPTIMIZATION OF BIOLOGY CHANGES EVERYTHING

IN 2013, JOSH HOFFMAN CO-FOUNDED Zymergen, a Bay Area-based company applying computation and automation to molecular systems in order to optimize industrial microbiology. Zymergen's platform is unique in that it enables precision engineering biology at industrial scale and quality to optimize existing products and produce new ones in agriculture, life sciences, and manufacturing.

JOHN CUMBERS: How does engineering of biology impact industry?

JOSH HOFFMAN: I believe that being able to reliably design, engineer, and optimize biology, biological systems will radically change the world. The question is, on what time scale? My own personal view is that the transformation will be as fundamental as the development of the semiconductor.

Engineered biology will change materials not only for clothing companies like Nike and Under Armour, but for the big consumer electronics companies like Apple and Samsung. They have to be thinking about it.

But, like the transformation of the chemical industry from natural products to petroleum-based products, it's going to happen over a 60- to 80-year timeframe. I don't think it's going to happen as quickly as the rise of mobile technologies, for example.

I think that precisely because I believe in the transformative power of biology, but I dislike the hype. I'm a short-term bear and long-term bull. I don't like the term synthetic biology, mostly because I don't think it applies to us. Honestly, there haven't been a lot of good investment outcomes associated with the term synthetic biology. Mostly, the term brings to mind misery and loss. And I'd prefer not to be associated with those failures.

Zymergen's solution is a deeply technology-focused approach. We're as much a technology company as a life sciences company. The nomenclature of synthetic biology doesn't pick that up. The term doesn't capture how Zymergen is both data side and biology focused. That's why I've never liked the term. It suggests that we're working on biofuels, which we are not.

KARL SCHMIEDER: Zymergen operates in the business-to-business world, could you describe what you do?

JOSH HOFFMAN: The thing that makes Zymergen unique is our ability to make biology work at scale in a cost effective, economically reasonable way.

I should preface that by saying there's been a substantial gap between the promise of the technology in the lab and the ability to make it work at scale. CEOs are skeptical of biotechnology because the promise has been clear since the *Time Magazine* cover in the late 1970s, early 1980s.[53] The problem is that industrial promise hasn't been realized because it's very difficult to make biology to work at scale.

As far as I know, we're the only company that's been able to economically, rapidly, and repeatedly show that we can make biology work at that industrial scale. We can do that to improve the economics of products that are already on the market, decrease the time it takes to get to market, and also to create new products.

KARL SCHMIEDER: Can you elaborate on that?

JOSH HOFFMAN: Our stuff works at scale more or less the first time out. A lot goes into the technology to make that possible. We're not selling a dream of a better tomorrow. We're selling better economics today. I believe with those better economics, comes the possibility of a better tomorrow.

JOHN CUMBERS: What makes Zymergen's approach unique?

JOSH HOFFMAN: Our approach is different from any other company I'm aware of. The software and data side of biology are as hard as any software data problem that exists in the world. At the same time, getting the automation to work on the life sciences side is probably harder than any automation problem.

We've built Zymergen to bring together the best and smartest individuals and created a culture that allows them to talk to each other. We're not looking for biologists who learned how to hack [the widely used programming language] Python while they were doing their Ph.D. We're looking for people who have experience solving big problems. For example, our Chief Technology Officer was the first non-founding engineer at Cloudera. Our V.P. of Engineering was a Director of Engineering at Twitter. That is the pedigree we're hiring on the software side because biology involves big data, and lots of data problems.

KARL SCHMIEDER: It is getting easier to engineer microbes but scale continues to be a rate-limiting step for many biotechnology projects. Do you think that will continue as biology gets easier to engineer and people are able to create microbes quickly that can produce a useful molecule?

JOSH HOFFMAN: That's right, putting a bug together is no longer rocket science. Most people work in yeast or *E. coli* because they are well understood, most of their genomes are annotated, but they are poor production hosts unless you're making ethanol. To be successful you first have to step out of the canonical hosts. Then you have to figure out how to improve the microbe.

The issue is most people who work in labs are working at small scale. Whether that's in a 384-well plate or a liter-sized bio-reactor, those are small scale. From an economics point of view, your microbe needs to work at the silo-sized, 10,000-liter fermenter scale.

We've solved those problems using data in a way that is highly predictive. That's a technology-based solution for a science-based problem.

A big part of the challenge is so little is understood of the genome. To scale, you need to make the changes to the genome that are going to improve performance. You just can't look at the place where you're inserting the sequence to produce your product. You need to be able to look across the entire genome.

We recently shipped a production host to a customer. It has a dozen changes—three or four were genes that were known to impact the production of the end product. The other changes were in genes that were unrelated and split evenly in three categories. One-third were genes that you could tell yourself impacted production. Another third were genes that had annotations, but in places where you had no idea why the gene's function impacted production. The final third were genes outside the annotation, genes of no known function.

Unless you have a way of searching the entire genome—because those genomes are big—you're probably not going to find those things. You need to do that in a data-driven way.

As you said, it's easy to engineer a microbe. You don't need a big data infrastructure to make the first bug. You could even climb up the performance curve doing it manually, but getting reliable performance at economic levels is a horse of a different color.

JASON KELLY: WE'RE BUILDING THE MICROBE DESIGN INDUSTRY

IN 2008, JASON KELLY, Ph.D., co-founded Ginkgo BioWorks with a group of peers from the Massachusetts Institute of Technology. The Boston-based company focuses on designing and developing organisms for use across industries and has developed an integrated technology platform that includes hardware, software, and wetware. Ginkgo BioWorks was the first biotechnology company to be admitted to Y-Combinator's[54] world-famous startup incubator. An outspoken supporter of genetic engineering,[55] Jason speaks frequently on the impact of synthetic biology.

KARL SCHMIEDER: Is there a business that won't be impacted by biotechnology?

JASON KELLY: Any company that has physical goods as part of its business needs to pay attention to biotech.

If you look at information technologies, every pure information business—from advertising agencies to big media companies—was impacted dramatically by digital. Every business that had a back office IT division was forced to change.

Biotech can serve a general purpose for manufacturing in the physical world the way computers are general purpose in an information-rich world. As we continue to get Moore's law improvements across biotech, the physical part of every business will see disruptions.

JOHN CUMBERS: Did you ever think twice about starting Ginkgo BioWorks versus going to work for any one of Boston's many biotech companies?

JASON KELLY: Today, what is called biotech really means biotechnology for developing medicines. Boston has many biotech pharmaceutical companies but when I was completing my Ph.D., I wasn't focused on discovering drugs or studying human physiology and disease.

When we started Ginkgo, we were focused on improving the tools for engineering biology. At the time there wasn't a fit for that at any Boston-based biotech company.

JOHN CUMBERS: What engineering principles are you applying to biology that haven't been applied with biotech previously?

JASON KELLY: There are two categories, microorganism design and the physical work of genetic engineering.

When it comes to the physical work of biotech—genetic engineering—we're using software and automation to do work that traditionally was done by bench scientists. This is by no means the first application of automation in biotech. The reading of DNA—DNA sequencing—for example, is a highly automated biotech process. The writing of DNA—DNA synthesis—is on its way to being highly automated.

With automation you trade off the flexibility of a process for the ease of scaling when you automate it. Automating a process that does a lot of things is harder than a process that will make the same thing every day.

At the end of the day, as long as you prepare it right, the DNA from different organisms looks the same. It goes through the same chemistry, the same processes, so you can scale that.

When you start to genetically engineer organisms, suddenly you have hundreds of protocols. If you want to insert DNA into the genome of an organism and you want to grow cells under certain conditions, you have to have scientists working at a bench. That is actually the hard part.

What's unique about what we do at Ginkgo is that we're applying engineering principles to standardize and automate the lab work of genetic engineering. We're not eliminating bench scientists, we're automating repetitive tasks so they can focus on design. The breadth of what we're automating is new.

KARL SCHMIEDER: One of the production bottlenecks in biotech has been measurement? Are you measuring the speed of the design-test-build cycle the way an agile tech startup would? Do you compare that to what's being automated?

JASON KELLY: Let me talk about measuring the success of organism engineering, then I'll tackle how we measure our work in the foundry.

Tom Knight, one of Ginkgo's co-founders, likes to say biology is nanotech that works. It really is nanotech.

As a result, you're operating at an extremely small scale. We're making changes to DNA. We can read it and we can write it. It's digital.

When you change the code, that can be reflected in the production of a gene that's converted to a protein. For example, an enzyme that is a functioning nano-machine that is very difficult to see. That's a general challenge in biology. You make a change to a genome, so how do you see the impact of that change?

The measurement technologies we need are extremely sophisticated. We use the latest technologies, like mass spectrometry, to get a picture of the changes we've made.

We've made huge investments into high-end analytics to give us a better view of the changes we've made to the organisms. Measurement is both very important and challenging because it's at the level of the organism itself.

Designers who change an organism's genome need to understand the impact of those changes to inform the next round of design. If you don't understand the impact of your design, you can't build the next iteration and learn.

We're investing a great deal to increase our capabilities in measurement and we'll continue those investments for the foreseeable future. It's a very important area of work for a biology-focused company.

With regard to the Foundry and how it operates, what we see happening at Ginkgo is a shift from what a scientist is doing at the bench today and what they'll be doing in 2018. The capabilities of biotechnology are advancing very rapidly. This is one of the reasons why I think industries outside pharmaceuticals really need to care about biotechnology.

The scientists are not just getting better. They're moving to a highly automated environment. We call that the Foundry and took that name from semiconductor foundries—precise, highly automated facilities. We have biotech foundries that can complete a certain lab protocol three-times cheaper in 2018 than they could in 2017.

We've been applying manufacturing process optimization in an automated, standardized environment that a scientist working at the bench could never do. Once every lab protocol is performed using robotics, you can track the exact quantity of every reagent, you can track every liquid transfer. You can track everything. You can apply statistical analysis to every protocol to find out which one worked, which one didn't. Then you apply quality control and improve your success rate.

This is run-of-the-mill process automation. It's standard manufacturing design optimization. The same thing has been done in the manufacturing of cars, semiconductors and everything else. We're taking the basic ideas of manufacturing, the assembly line—automation, standardization, measurement—and applying it to biological operations. Once you have that corpus of data, you can optimize. We're creating our own version of Moore's law with genetic engineering because we're measuring processes that until now have been done with no metrics.

KARL SCHMIEDER: How do you apply standardization and automation to organism design?

JASON KELLY: The analogy of DNA as code holds up really well. It's a digital code. An organism essentially compiles and uses the code to execute multiple functions.

It's pretty messy inside cells. All the functions bump into each other. You can't isolate protocols or software libraries from each other. But at the end of the day, it's digital. You can read it clearly, you can write it clearly, and you can program it.

We still have a lot to learn on microbial programming, on designing DNA code compared to what's been done in the software industry. There are a lot of lessons to learn from the writing of modern software. Biology, however, is extremely complicated but there are analogies and lessons.

Our Foundry takes lessons from manufacturing and semi-conductor manufacturing. On the DNA design side, we're learning from software programming and applying those lessons to biology.

JOHN CUMBERS: What will Ginkgo look like in 20 years?

JASON KELLY: I talk about the semiconductor industry a lot. Semiconductors are found in many products. They're in your computer, your phone, your car, your TV. We have a semi-conductor industry that is in the business of designing and producing semiconductors that end up in many other products. We think the same thing will happen with microbes.

At the end of the day, the design and manufacturing of a semiconductor looks more similar than different no matter where you're using that semiconductor. That's why there is a semiconductor industry. It didn't make sense for every industry to develop its own semiconductor design and manufactured capability. It is smarter to engage with the semiconductor industry and learn how to apply what they make to your product.

We believe there will be an organism design industry. Companies will specialize in the design of organisms. Maybe those companies will end up splitting based on the tree of life. I have no idea how they'll split.

In the near-term, Ginkgo believes that if you're going to use an engineered microbe in a process, you'd be better off dealing with the microbe design industry, rather than hiring 30 scientists and trying to create it in your own lab. That's not going to make a lot of sense when the economics of the Foundry and our learnings are so much better than anything you could build in-house. It will be more efficient for you to engage with us so that we design your microbes for you. Then you can deploy those organisms as part of your industry, which you know better than we do.

In the next five years, I'd like there to be a recognition that a microbe design industry exists and you'd be silly to design your own.

Predicting twenty years from now is a lot harder. We'll be a lot better at design and will be creating much more complicated organisms and doing all sorts of fun stuff.

If Ginkgo designs the microbe, who builds it? Foundries build the building blocks.

but that is exactly what fabless semiconductor companies do.

fabs TSM, Samsung build them. Some do both.

GEORGE CHURCH: WE'LL BE CRISPR GENE-EDITING ADULTS SOON

GEORGE CHURCH, Ph.D., is a professor at Harvard & MIT, has co-authored 425 papers, written 95 patent publications, and the book *Regenesis*. A leader in synthetic biology, Dr. Church, developed methods used for the first genome sequence and has been responsible for million-fold cost reductions in sequencing. He's also worked on barcoding, DNA assembly from chips, genome editing, writing and recoding and has been involved in founding, co-founding, and advising dozens of companies.

KARL SCHMIEDER: You wrote and published *Regenesis* **in 2012, then updated the book in 2014. Since you published the book, what developments have most excited you?**

GEORGE CHURCH: I wanted to get people to think outside of the box in a way that wasn't science fiction. I also wanted to show how you could turn science fiction into something practical very quickly.

For example, according to Moore's Law next generation sequencing should have taken six decades. It only took six years. The idea of using synthetic biology to create a brain-computer interface was seen as science fiction. Now, it's a major component of the BRAIN[56] initiative. The idea of writing and editing genomes seemed far out. Then CRISPR hit and within two years, it went from idea to three Cambridge-based companies with a market cap of $2 billion.

We're on a very steep exponential [curve], making it hard to regulate, hard to invest, and even hard to keep up. As citizens, we need to keep up. Doing nothing is not a solution.

JOHN CUMBERS: You've been a pioneer in synthetic biology for more than 15 years. How would you rate our progress in making biology easier to engineer?

GEORGE CHURCH: I would argue that synthetic biology hasn't followed the path of the original vision, which fragmented into multiple paths. One was the shared vision to make biology easier to engineer, but you also had the biomimetics people, the origin of life synthetic biology people, and the bio-circuitry people. There also were the stochastic folks and genome engineers.

The bio-circuitry group got a lot of attention. That's where you create some DNA that's analogous to an electronic circuit, a Von Neumann device, inside a living cell. You can create flip-flop circuits, logic gates and oscillators, but that isn't what biology does well and it's not a great example of what synthetic biology can do. It also has underperformed.

What has outperformed is the exponentials for reading and writing DNA. DNA synthesis and sequencing have improved about three-million fold. DNA editing has improved by a factor of 100 or more.

The engineering discipline of synthetic biology is still close to that discipline we've call genetic engineering or recombinant DNA. In that discipline, you bash away at natural capabilities using a full set of knowledge in an intuitive way. It has a few things in common with the most creative areas of other engineering disciplines. But it's not the manual full of spec sheets that some of the electrical engineers in synthetic biology had imagined. We're not there yet and might not need to go there.

For example, if I were to make an organ, I would engineer the pig so that it could donate organs to humans. We do that. Nothing about that strikes you as taking a page from a Silicon Valley microfabrication booklet.

If we set morphology as one example of advances in this field, then we are starting to see some efforts in synthetic developmental biology and synthetic neurobiology. Groups like mine are building organoids by reverse engineering the code that the developmental systems use. We're trying to accelerate them because the faster they can go, the faster we can debug them and make them highly parallel, so that we can test billions simultaneously. Once we do that, we'll be in a position to have a morphological engineering discipline with tremendous capacity.

One of the advantages that biology has over other disciplines is we can we can do trial and error better than civil, aerospace, mechanical, or electrical engineering. In those disciplines, it's fairly common to have one major prototype and a few minor ones. With biology you can make billions to trillions of prototypes. Our destiny may be not to become similar to other engineering disciplines, but to teach them how to be different, how to have more trial and error.

KARL SCHMIEDER: You've been outspoken when it comes to editing the human germline. Could you explain why?

GEORGE CHURCH: The point I make about human germline editing is that if we aren't careful, we draw boundary lines in counter-productive places. People have a tendency to dismiss certain things by saying that we don't have to worry about them because it's too difficult or it's not going to happen. Using CRISPR to edit the germ line is one of those.

When it comes to editing humans, people get hung up on editing embryos. The fact is if we're going to edit the germline, it's more likely to happen and be helpful if done in sperm.

In 2015, people were saying nobody is going to edit the germline because it puts embryos at risk. That year, I presented at the National Academy of Sciences and said, "If you engineer stem cells you can test those in your lab to make sure your edits are precise, not a heterogeneous mosaic." Then, you put those back in the male testis. It goes through normal meiosis and development, makes sperm. From that point on, the male can fertilize eggs and create babies that are absolutely normal. You've eliminated his carrier status for recessive disease without putting embryos at risk.

This completely flipped the standard ethical argument on its head. I think this is part of the reason why the National Academy of Sciences February 2017 report[57] acknowledged germ line editing is not the problem. In their opinion, enhancement is the problem but I have a counter argument.

JOHN CUMBERS: What is that?

GEORGE CHURCH: The red line everyone was drawing was between germline and somatic cells. They then changed to noting valid medical applications for germline editing. In particular, the one I had proposed, so you can save embryos from abortion, IVF (in vitro fertilization) and even natural abortion. They said, "Augmentation is where we draw the line." They said, "We're only going to allow saving people from medical problems."

Starting in 2012, I pointed out that when you're trying to cure someone with a muscular or brain disease, you're trying to get them from sick to normal. But you can't aim for normal because that's like trying to put an adequate amount of food on the table for guests, you're likely to put out a little more just in case. You're going to aim for a little above normal. Or, you might aim for normal and some will randomly land just above normal. Are those people enhanced?

Let's say you create a drug that fights cognitive decline and you can get patients back to normal memory levels. What happens if that drug is used off-label by someone who doesn't have cognitive decline? They might be augmented. And if these are safe and effective, where are the ethical concerns? This isn't sports where there are rules. The rules are, it's safe and effective, and no embryos are involved.

You can debug a procedure [pre-birth] that takes a person twenty years to reach maturity, but that's not nearly as interesting, or concerning, as a gene-editing procedure you can do on an adult and get significant changes in weeks to months. Gene-editing technology will spread much faster in adults.

KARL SCHMIEDER: If there were a tool or technology that would make biology engineering easier, what would that be?

GEORGE CHURCH: I'd like a tool to easily measure morphology and functionality. A tool that can screen and select for everything you can imagine. Part of the cleverness of design is the ability to debug and check the main design.

In addition to the exponential advances [we've seen] in reading and writing genomes, we're working on ways to miniaturize testing. We can now test about 10^{13} genomes or templates for genotype/phenotype correlations. That's 10 trillion prototypes simultaneously. That's the practical maximum we can test right now. Then you can quickly create two or three iterations in a few days. We're way beyond where we thought we'd be and I'm looking forward to where we're going.

RICHARD KITNEY: EVERY BUSINESS WILL FEEL THE IMPACT OF SYNTHETIC BIOLOGY

RICHARD KITNEY WAS A FOUNDING member of the British Government's working group on the development of a roadmap for synthetic biology in the United Kingdom. Recognized globally as a leader in the field, he serves as Chairman of the Institute of Systems and Synthetic Biology and Principal Investigator and Co-Director of the Imperial College, London Synthetic Biology Hub and SynbiCITE.

KARL SCHMIEDER: The United Kingdom has been a pioneer in biotechnology, can you describe SynbiCITE and the focus on synthetic biology?

RICHARD KITNEY: In the fall of 2012, there was a call to establish a national industrial translation center for synthetic biology in the U.K. We were among a number of universities that applied and we were successful in obtaining the center. We received the funding in 2013. Since then, we've set up a center that includes three components designed to support and help grow small-to-medium-sized U.K. companies. The three components include:

First, providing equipment and expert personnel who can support subject matter experts and startups.

Second, funding for proof of concept projects. That funding is typically about US$75,000 for six months. If the company is successful, they can apply for a grant of US$300,000 that is matched by an external source or industry. We're now working on an accelerator as part of that process. It's called BioStart.

Third, providing business courses. For example, we'll run a one-day course on how to write a business plan. We teach students what is intellectual property, what is the company structure of those running through our version of the Lean LaunchPad, which we developed and run with Jerry Engle and Steve Blank. We also run a 4-day MBA.

When we first started, we used to run all these tracks in parallel. Now we do them serially, so that funding continues only for companies that have completed the appropriate courses.

The second U.K. road map for synthetic biology was published in February 2016. It's called Bio Design for the Bio Economy. That is now being funded and being incorporated in the U.K. government's new industrial strategy. The U.K. plans to invest £1 billion over the next two–three years to encourage commercial development—not just in synthetic biology but across the board. It may not sound like a lot of money but it is a departure from the way the commercialization of science was previously funded.

JOHN CUMBERS: How is that different from the way things were done in the past?

RICHARD KITNEY: We have had a tendency in the U.K. to invest in basic research without the follow-up necessary to commercialize basic research. I'd like to see more public funding to help early-stage companies get through the so-called valley of death before they commercialize their product. Innovate U.K. is meeting those needs, but, in my opinion, the U.K. could do a better job of that.

JOHN CUMBERS: Is biology a technology? How do you think it will change over the next 20 to 50 years?

RICHARD KITNEY: Synthetic biology is a technology, but we're at an early stage. Clearly, the modern era of biology goes back to Watson and Crick. But, for me, the field didn't come into its own until 2001 with the initial sequencing of the human genome and our ability to write DNA chemically. That's why I say we're at an early stage.

The ability to read and write DNA is analogous to the importance of the invention of the printing press and the revolution in knowledge that resulted. Our ability to read and write DNA opens up a new perspective on biological-based technology. We're just at the beginning.

What about in 20 to 50 years? It's really, really hard to predict but the use of biology as a technology is going to be unbelievably important. Look at the invention of the transistor in 1947. It was impossible to predict what would happen as a result of that invention. Who could foresee the impact of computers, digital technologies, the internet, smartphones, and everything else. The same is true with biology. It will have a massive impact.

JOHN CUMBERS: Is biology an engineering discipline at the moment?

RICHARD KITNEY: I don't think it's an engineering discipline at the moment but it is rapidly becoming one. It absolutely needs to become one.

I'm a biological engineer so I have an engineering background. Biological engineering is very different from biology. Chemical engineering is very different from chemistry. In both cases, each field is incredibly important. It's no accident that major universities, including Imperial College, have separate departments for these disciplines.

The analogy holds true for biology, synthetic biology, and engineered biology. Applying standardization and characterization, feedback control systems, and the design-build-learn cycle turn synthetic biology into an engineering discipline.

KARL SCHMIEDER: Do you have any examples of those principles being applied either in academia or industry?

RICHARD KITNEY: Prokarium is a good example of applying that approach. They've developed an oral vaccine platform that takes an antigen from a gene sequence, delivers it to the gut, where it produces an immune response. That required applying feedback and control principles to design a system that produces a vaccine in the gut.

There are examples of companies developing bio-sensors designed according to engineering principles. At Imperial College, we've designed sensors to detect bacterial infections and cystic fibrosis. We're also seeing very advanced modeling being applied to biology. For example, there are companies in Singapore working with GSK to develop models that can be used commercially.

KARL SCHMIEDER: What do you think non-biotech businesses need to understand about these technologies and their potential impact?

RICHARD KITNEY: Most people don't understand how our ability to read and write DNA right now opens up the possibility of designing biology. They don't understand bio-design is real.

This will have major implications for a wide range of businesses. You name it, it will be impacted.

In lectures, I like to look at the development of synthetic chemistry in the middle of the 1800s. Synthetic chemistry plus the use of oil drove the development of most of the major industries of the 20th Century.

Non-biotech businesses need to appreciate that when you begin replacing oil with bio-based feedstocks and couple that with the rise of synthetic biology or engineered biology, you will see new industries arise.

Over the course of the next 20 to 50 years, we're going to see as many if not more products developed than in the 20th Century. They will be engineered, biology based and biologically manufactured. This represents a massive increase in the economy.

KINKEAD REILING: BIOLOGY'S PROGRESS TOWARD ENGINEERING DISCIPLINE WILL AMAZE YOU

KINKEAD REILING, Ph.D., co-founded Amyris, a leader in biofuels and biochemicals in 2003. He served as Senior Vice President of Corporate Development until early 2011. Prior to founding Amyris, he worked as a postdoctoral scholar in the UC Berkeley Chemical Engineering Department developing microbial production systems for anti-malarial and anti-cancer therapeutic compounds.

JOHN CUMBERS: What do you think non-biotech businesses need to understand about the impact of new biotechnologies on their businesses?

KINKEAD REILING: You have to define how broad you want to go or what company or industry you want to impact. In most cases, whether they know it or not, non-biotech businesses have been improved by biology.

Let me give you an example with Caterpillar. They are as far from a biotechnology company as any company, but biotech is already impacting their employees. Whether it's health or food, biotechnology helps Caterpillar's people improve their lives. As a result, their productivity will go up.

Computers helped Caterpillar increase their productivity. Armed with computers and data, the people at Caterpillar radically improved the company. I find that intriguing.

In the short-term Caterpillar's core business—tractors and bulldozers—eventually will need to be adapted to crops that are being grown with biotechnology. Fifty years from now, longer-term, the bulldozers go away and they will be using engineered biology to do the work those bulldozers once did.

For me, the biggest impact on non-biotech businesses will be on people and their health in the near-term. Longer-term, things get more questionable and you start moving markets.

KARL SCHMIEDER: That's near-term and long-term. How do you think biology impacts workers and productivity in the medium-term in the next 10 to 15 years?

KINKEAD REILING: If people are healthier, they have fewer sick days so productivity is going to go up. This isn't limited to traditional biotech—it can be health-related—but it has an impact. If people in the workplace live longer, they stay in their roles longer. You do less retraining. That's one trend that we can connect with today.

Medium-term biotech is changing traditional agriculture. It's improving yields. It's making food healthier.

Longer-term—instead of having to manufacture tractors, we grow them.

That a little science fiction but I think it's what people like to think about, longer-term. I'm more interested in the short-term, the awesome impact on people in the workplace. I don't hear people talking about the short-term impact on workers.

JOHN CUMBERS: How have things progressed to make biology more of an engineering discipline?

KINKEAD REILING: There's an amazing talk by the guy who is planning the Mission to Mars. He said engineering offers a relatively good set of rules. I think biology has been an engineering discipline for a while. We've been narrowing the error bars to reduce uncertainty. In principle, that makes things more financially attractive.

For example, Amyris was one of the first biological engineering businesses. Now, there's a new set of companies that are in biological engineering. At each phase of the life cycle they get more predictable in their ability to deliver a product created with biology.

KARL SCHMIEDER: Could you give a picture of how that changed when you founded Amyris and where things are now?

KINKEAD REILING: Sure. A long time ago as someone who had this crazy idea of using ethanol as fuel and wanted to figure how to create it from corn. There was a 20-year process to get right. There was a shorter process to get Amyris' diesel substitute—it's not yet there but there's been progress. It'd be interesting to compare the decrease in the cost of DNA synthesis compared to the decrease in the cost of bringing a biological process from ideation to process.

KARL SCHMIEDER: A curve would be useful but I suspect people would ask, "What does that curve really mean?"

KINKEAD REILING: People used to ask, "Why does quantum mechanics matter?" But as hard drives got smaller, there is a quantum effect that allowed them to shrink and store more information per square inch. Now, we've moved onto solid state drives but quantum mechanics—because it was tangible—meant something to anyone working on a computer. It'd be nice to have the same thing with bio-engineering.

I would argue that there is an odd and inaccurate co-location of the psyche of engineering that says, I need a small amount of money to develop a product. People argue the fact that engineers need multiple billions of dollars to create a new airplane.

Biology as an engineering discipline doesn't mean it's cheap. It just means it's a bit more predictable. Just because biology is an engineering discipline, doesn't mean that someone in a garage is going to develop a product for $20,000.

Biology as an engineering discipline means I can creatively and predictably, for a given number of dollars, give you a really awesome product.

SUZANNE LEE: FUTURE FASHION IS BIOFABRICATED

SUZANNE LEE STARTED GROWING MICROBIAL materials in 2003. Shortly thereafter, she founded Biocouture, the first biocreative consultancy. In 2014, Suzanne started Biofabricate, an annual summit to bring designers, biologists and technologists together. The author of *Fashioning the Future: Tomorrow's Wardrobe*, she has been a TED Senior Fellow, a Launch Material Innovator, an initiative of NASA, USAID and the State Department. Suzanne currently serves as the Chief Creative Officer at Modern Meadow.

KARL SCHMIEDER: You were trained as a textile and digital designer, how has that influenced your thinking about biotechnology?

SUZANNE LEE: In 2002, I was writing *Fashioning the Future*, a look at fashion in 50 years time. The fashion industry is entirely focused on next season or the next two seasons, so you can't envision the future talking to fashion designers. You get insights from people developing the materials of the future, and the manufacturing technologies of the future.

I happened to be attending a Ph.D. presentation at the London College of Fashion, where I met an advisor who was a materials scientist. When I explained the premise of the book, he suggested I turn to fermentation and biotechnology. He suggested the materials of the future would be produced using microorganisms. He painted an image of garments growing in a vat. That blew my mind.

From that moment on, I focused on the Biocouture project. We applied for and received a grant for a biotech-design collaboration and very quickly started growing sheets using kombucha. The simple process we used yielded material with amazing properties, though it needed tuning. It needed to be more elastic, more hydrophobic.

I started looking for solutions. I met Paul Freemont and Richard Kitney at Imperial College and showed them the materials we had grown. Paul introduced me to synthetic biology and I started to see the possibilities of designing and engineering an organism as the first step in a design project.

The light bulb moment for me was understanding that design starts when you have mastery over DNA, the ultimate creative tool. When you see scientists reading and writing DNA the same way software developers do, you realize synthetic biology is the future of materials. It is the answer to optimizing capabilities and performance of materials and manufacturing.

KARL SCHMIEDER: You're one of two designers who have a senior role at a biotech company. Why should biotechnology companies consider adding that role?

SUZANNE LEE: Christina Agapakis at Ginkgo BioWorks is a friend. The big difference between us—and we've talked about this many times—is that I come to biotechnology with an art background. Christina comes to design with a biotechnology background.

Art school teaches you to think in a specific way. Explore by doing. Challenge everything. You don't set out with a hypothesis the way you do with science. You start by playing. It's a different way of working.

I see biotechnology as the ultimate creative tool. The products of the future will come from engaging with the creative process at the very beginning. Understanding that you can engineer a protein and design its structure to give your end product specific characteristics.

Fashion is very simplistic. It's focused on designing the handbag. For me, what's exciting is the possibility of bringing design, research and development into the scientific realm.

KARL SCHMIEDER: How does this work at Modern Meadow? How do the designers and scientists work with each other?

SUZANNE LEE: We have an incredible team of scientists who are developing new-to-the-world processes. Interestingly, few team members understand the leather industry, the accessories or products that our materials would go into. It's interesting to work with designers who are learning bio-fabrication, then pushing and pulling the process in ways the scientists would have never imagined.

That's why you need the creatives in a company like Modern Meadow. It's probably not the case for other biotech companies but it is for us. We were founded to produce materials like leather that you will wear. If you didn't have someone on the team that understands materials, how they perform, how they are used, you couldn't develop new materials with new features and aesthetics.

The scientists realize this is very different from any other biotech company. It adds to the appeal. They've never had the opportunity to work with people who think so differently. People think we're special and we stand out. It's definitely a selling point for recruiting. We're attracting scientists who find the idea of design intriguing. Most of them never imagined that.

KARL SCHMIEDER: What should non-biotech companies know about biofabrication? How could that make them more sustainable, differentiated companies?

SUZANNE LEE: There is a big education component to my job. A key challenge is helping consumer brands understand how the world is changing.

The history of materials is human history. Until now, you've had two ways of making things: natural and man-made. In the 20th century, you had agricultural crops, animal products, and plastics from oil. Each was its own world.

Biotech allows us to bring the best of those worlds together. The building blocks of nature, the proteins and carbohydrates, can be designed or engineered to have the same properties as synthetics. This opens up a new material age. That is quite mind blowing for companies that are trying to solve supply chain issues, companies thinking about cradle-to-cradle or closed-loop manufacturing, or looking for sustainable materials.

There are many reasons why these solutions are interesting to potential consumers but educating them around bio-fabrication, how it delivers and drives innovation, is also very exciting. We still have to educate them that we're not just replacing natural products, but have the opportunity to be creative in developing and producing things that haven't been possible until now.

KARL SCHMIEDER: In addition to your work at Modern Meadow, you've organized the Biofabricate conference for three years.[58] During that period what progress have you seen?

SUZANNE LEE: I spent 10 years as a foreigner in this field, attending conferences with scientists and telling them more people need to know about this field. You certainly couldn't send designers to those conferences. It would all go over their heads. To have impact, we needed to speak to the average person, to help them understand the opportunities. There was a conversation waiting to happen.

In 2013, I decided we needed a conference to engage people outside of the sciences. In 2014, we held the first Biofabricate in New York City. It was very successful and started the conversation.

Since then, the progress has been huge. We've started to see the first prototypes emerge from the biofabrication companies. For example, Bolt Threads just launched its spider silk tie. It tells a consumer story that people can engage with.

Last year, Adidas launched their first bio-fabricated shoe. The moment you have a big brand make an announcement like that, the reach expands. You start to engage with designers and other brands in ways that the field of synthetic biology couldn't on its own. Everyone understands a sports shoe. First, you talk about the shoe, how it's different, and what it means for everything we do. It goes way beyond the shoe, the clothes. You suddenly have a story about an item that is so quotidian that your mom can relate to it. That's how we've gone from petri dishes to what we're going to wear. Now, we have collaborations with big global brands. That is a huge trajectory.

In 2016, Ecovative and BioMason, who both attended the first Biofabricate Conference, came together and launched a product together. It's a bacterial glue product that pairs with the materials Ecovative grows from mycelium. I see that as a picture of how we reimagine everything that we design using different organisms to give us materials with different properties. I'm looking forward to seeing more of this rapid progress.

KARL SCHMIEDER: What challenges does Modern Meadow currently face?

SUZANNE LEE: As of this moment, we're looking to recruit the next generation of designers and it's been difficult. We've visited every design student grad show and can't find anyone. There are no universities that offer coursework that teach designers and scientists together. Designers don't have the basic lab skills and scientists don't have the basic design skills. There are only a few companies hiring people with the expertise we seek. It's a huge gap for us.

Higher education is lagging behind state-of-the-art technology and needs to wake up. Schools are not equipping designers with the skills they need for this industry.

On the commercial side of design, we need to educate designers on the role of biofabrication—especially early in the design process. We grapple with this every day. Consumer brands and designers need to understand that Modern Meadow is not a materials supplier. We work as R&D partners. We partner with brands that understand the R&D process to co-develop products. That means identifying specifications for performance and aesthetics. All of our commercial relationships started as R&D partnerships.

KARL SCHMIEDER: What challenges does synthetic biology face?

SUZANNE LEE: Messaging and communications could do a better job addressing the real fears that people have. We could do that by telling more success stories. Consumer success stories are important because most people don't—and won't—care about the scientific or technical innovations behind their products.

This field offers new solutions to big planetary problems. Rather than speaking to ourselves all the time, we need more people to communicate to the public. We need to tell the stories, solutions, and interesting opportunities. Those stories need to be told in ways that connect with people on a level they can understand without making them feel stupid.

I think those of us in the field really underestimate this because it's new and it's been academic. Scientists do not grasp the communications challenges and the need for stories. Companies like ours and the people defining the field need to speak about biofabrication in a way that is much more inspirational and aspirational.

ANDREW HESSEL: ENGINEERING LIVING ORGANISMS WILL BE THE WORLD'S BIGGEST INDUSTRY

ANDREW HESSEL, Ph.D., is a futurist at the forefront of synthetic biology. Trained in microbiology and genetics, he helps industry, academics and authorities better understand changes in the life sciences. He serves as the Distinguished Researcher with Autodesk Life Sciences. Andrew is one of the founders of Genome Project-Write, an open, international project overseeing the engineering and testing of large genomes in cell lines.

JOHN CUMBERS What do you think the biggest impact Genome Project-Write will have on humanity?

ANDREW HESSEL: We see writing a genome as the core technology for genetic engineering. It will supercharge the entire field. It will require the creation of better software design tools, better DNA synthesis and assembly technologies, and better test technologies. The project will accelerate the research and development necessary to engineer metabolisms, cells, tissues, and organisms. It will also launch countless careers, unlock new economic resources, and impact almost every industry. Engineering living organisms will be one of the world's largest, new industries.

Last year, we changed the name from Human Genome Project-Write to Genome Project-Write because people were already working with different model organisms and we didn't want to exclude the synthesis of any genome.

In the 1980s, I remember following the launch of the Human Genome Project. I thought the idea of being able to read and write biology was awesome. At the time I was paying the bills by working with computers. Digital technologies make it possible for us to design the world around us. Digital technologies have turned biology into a different field and allow us to design living things.

KARL SCHMIEDER: How will industries be disrupted by our ability to engineer biology?

ANDREW HESSEL: I expect to see major changes in multiple industries. For example, the biopharmaceutical industry already depends on biotechnology for its new product pipeline. Drug development will be touched by engineered biology across all disease categories.

In materials, we've tapped very few of the materials that biology can manufacture. Our ability to engineer biology will allow us to reach deep into the biological world and create novel materials better than those in nature.

Food is the place where biology touches us each and every day. It's the first medicine. You are what you eat. The way we produce food is going to change radically based on our ability to engineer biology.

Our health depends on more than food. It also depends on our environment. We are living machines. The more we learn to harness living machines to maintain us and the environment, the closer we'll come to achieving balance with nature. Right now, we're changing the balance with nature faster than nature can compensate.

We're in the early days of biology and electronics merging, but it's happening at an almost every level. We are already attaching molecules to electronic systems and soon will create machines that interface with human brains. This is going to be much bigger than people can imagine.

The semiconductor and electronics industries will get closer to the engineered biology community. I've been going to the SemiSynBio Meetings for years. It's one of my favorite meetings because it's where these two very powerful technologies come together to figure each other out.

Regulation should become an industry. It's not right now, but it should be. Regulations are being disrupted because the current framework for oversight and regulations doesn't work. As technologies accelerate, it's going to get more difficult. Regulatory is adjacent to biosecurity, which also will become its own industry.

JOHN CUMBERS: Could you give us a vision of products that might come from the industries you mentioned?

ANDREW HESSEL: I want to be able to upload new genetic code into my cells. There's no other way to stop diseases than by getting a new code into damaged cells, so I've been looking at nanoparticles as delivery mechanisms.

In the consumer space, look at how cellphones have changed. In the movie Wall Street, Michael Douglas is using one of the first cell phones on the beach. It's a giant brick. Over time, cell phones have gotten smaller, and the telephone part is just a tiny chip. If we continue to shrink the cell phone, soon, they will be the size of a mitochondria. The average human hair is 75 microns across, a mitochondria is one to ten microns in size. Maybe one day, every cell can have its own electronic cell phone.

Or maybe we'll be able to program cells to make their own phones. We're just starting to build biological circuits. The circuits are very simple. When you start putting those circuits together, you get a radio. Add more circuits and you get a bi-directional radio—a phone.

Either way, imagine being able to communicate with every cell in your body. Then you can ask any cell, "How are you feeling?" After a weekend of hard partying, your liver can tell you it needs a break. You get the idea? It's a self-cellphone.

Our ability to build biological circuits is revolutionary and it's not a hundred years away. We could plot a graph on the electronics side to predict how long it will take. We're very smart with electronics and good at making predictions. On the biological side, it's less predictable but it will get better soon with more data.

Another idea. When my daughter was born a few years ago, we were frustrated because my wife couldn't produce enough milk. Babies are made of [and subsist on] milk. That's all they eat for the first seven-eight months of life. Breast milk has huge immunological and developmental benefits. Yet, there are few options for mothers if they can't produce milk. Breast milk banks are not regulated. There's a grey market for breast milk but people cheat and adulterate the samples. Formula is literally a chemical mixture that tastes horrible.

I wanted engineered breast milk and became an advisor to MuuFri (now named Perfect Day) since they're using yeast to engineer milk. It's not their focus right now, but maybe one day. In the meantime, there's another startup, BioNascent, that has set their sights on making a better infant formula.

Wouldn't it be better to have a creature, something furry and warm, that had the ability to produce perfect breast milk? A non-sentient, biological organism that has been engineered to produce milk nutritionally equivalent to mother's milk? A milk Tribble like in Star Trek?[59] That type of technology would be awesome for babies.

KARL SCHMIEDER: Is there a biological technology that you wished you had?

ANDREW HESSEL: I want the enzymatic DNA synthesizer that will be at least a thousand times better than what we have today. Next-generation sequencing technology massively accelerated our ability to read DNA. An enzymatic DNA synthesizer could be the equivalent accelerator for engineered biology. If you can synthesize DNA faster, then you can conduct more experiments and learn faster. That's what I'd like to see. More people programming life.

R.J. KIRK: BIOTECHNOLOGY IS THE GREATEST INDUSTRIAL VECTOR EVER

RANDAL J. KIRK IS THE Chairman and CEO of Intrexon, a company that has developed genetically modified salmon, an apple that never browns, and a modified strain of mosquito designed to combat *Aedes aegypti* mosquitoes that can spread yellow fever, dengue fever, and Zika fever viruses and other diseases. R.J. gave a very well-received keynote at SynBioBeta San Francisco 2015 and keynoted the Seventh International Meeting on Synthetic Biology.

JOHN CUMBERS: You recently spoke at the Borlaug World Food Prize[60] on technophobia—why is that so important to understand?

R.J. KIRK: I am making the point that man has always been afraid of new technologies. Man has always been technophobic. From pre-history to today, there has been a fear of technology whether implicit or explicit.

So the real question is, how do you overcome technophobia?

You have to understand technophobia is broadly conserved socially. It must be—in part—genetic. Once you understand fear of new technologies it becomes possible to manage that fear. As a species, we manage fear—though sometimes better than others.

The history of mankind is the history of this technology, so it is irrefutable that initially frightening new technologies do sometimes get adopted.

Most of us are able to overcome our fear of a technology when we see that the benefits outweigh the risks. Today, I'm talking to you on an iPhone. Any smart hacker could access my iPhone and read all the emails on this device. There also is an increased frequency of glioma associated with cell phone use. Like most of us, I've made a risk-benefit calculation and accept the tangible benefits I receive from the technology. There is probably no technology that is cost- and risk-free. Certainly, this is true of the wheel and of fire, technologies that certainly have their downsides.

So, how do we as technology developers overcome society's fear of technology? One way is by providing tangible benefits—benefits that consumers will genuinely appreciate. Developers of new technology must convey tangible consumer benefits so people can evaluate risk-benefit and choose for themselves.

Many years ago, I was on a panel sponsored by [the financial services company] VISA. They wanted to understand how concerned people were about the loss of privacy resulting from a worldwide network of ATM machines. They were concerned people wouldn't want their personal banking information available through a vast client-server computer system. We all know the history of ATM machines. They're everywhere. People were willing to give up a loss of privacy for the convenience of accessing cash anywhere.

KARL SCHMIEDER: What can technology developers do to manage that fear of the new?

R.J. KIRK: Manage the asset. Be transparent. Engage your audience.

Think about what Facebook is doing now around fake news. They're being transparent and addressing the issue head-on. A few years ago, when cyberbullying became a national issue, they went through something similar. It was a nasty situation with Congresspeople proposing legislation against social media.

Facebook responded by hiring people and managing that aspect of their business. They're doing this now and I hope they will continue to do so in the future.

Companies like Google and Facebook have taught us how to navigate a new technology through society. One of the main lessons is that transparency and engagement are really good things. People will reward you for being transparent and for engaging the public.

KARL SCHMIEDER: Do you think managing the asset is any different for biotechnology compared to digital technologies?

R.J. KIRK: Not fundamentally different but the stakes are much higher for biotechnology. Biotechnology is the greatest industrial vector ever. Its implications are the most profound. This will have far ranging implications for how we feed our population, what sorts of lives we lead, what condition the planet is in and even how we feel about life. These are far more important matters than anything that someone is going to tweet you.

Let's say we get in my time machine and go back to Palo Alto 1983. We have a conversation with Gordon Moore, Intel's co-founder. At the time, Moore is transitioning Intel from a memory chip company to a company focused almost entirely on microprocessors. We ask him, "How are these microprocessors going to be used? What are the implications? How will this change society?"

He would have been able to name dozens of examples that by now have proved true. The one thing that probably would not have predicted is the device that I'm holding in my hand—my iPhone. In terms of technology uptake, the smartphone is the most rapidly adopted technology in the history of the world. On the numbers, it is the most significant contribution of information technology to the world and yet it cannot begin to compare in impact to a technology that will determine our health, our food, our environment, and indeed the health of the entire planet.

JOHN CUMBERS: Do you have any examples of a biotechnology company managing an asset the way you've described?

R.J. KIRK: Sure, Intrexon. Our non-browning Arctic Apple seems to be the single most consumer-preferred, media-preferred, regulator-preferred GMO food in history. One reason for this is, I believe, the way that Neal Carter has developed it and talked about it, shown it, demonstrated it, let people experience it, while always being truthful and forthright about it. People see its advantages and they want it, and without feeling like they are being duped, but rather making an intelligent choice for a healthy, wholesome and delicious apple. Of course it is GMO, but I do not know anyone who has tried it and not loved it.

JOHN CUMBERS: Intrexon cooperated with the creation of a venture fund around technologies that you develop internally? How is that different from other corporate venture funds?

R.J. KIRK: It is somewhat the reverse of a corporate venture fund. Intrexon has labs with more than 1000 employees in the United

States, Canada and Europe. We don't have a corporate headquarters. We have lots of products under development at any given time. Our scientific teams are incredibly creative and bright, and new ideas come out of our labs all the time. We do some internal product development, but not every interesting or meritorious idea can be developed by us or even by our corporate partners.

The fund was created to invest in ideas otherwise not being backed by Intrexon for product development, ideas that need funding in the $5 million to $10 million range. It helps us to determine if an internal idea can become a business. In consequence, investors benefit when something good happens. If one of our team has a compelling idea and they can get to proof of principle, then proof of concept on a small budget, then it might start to look like a VC SpinCo opportunity. The fund provides a discipline around those opportunities because it is externally managed by professional fund managers (JMP Securities).

In addition, the fund makes it easier for us to enter into partnerships. Our business model relies to a considerable extent on partnering to develop our projects. Partnerships, whether small or large—like our collaborations with Merck KgaA or Janssen Pharmaceuticals—require more or less the same degree of administrative efforts so the natural tendency would be for us to stay away from small deals. Yet over the course of my career I've seen small deals can turn into very big deals many times. I don't want to lose those opportunities.

The fund allows many of those deals to be housed under one roof, greatly simplifying the administrative interface over a diversity of opportunities. The fund managers can decide what to do with the winners. They can hire enterprise management. They could IPO. They could sell to a major company. Meanwhile, Intrexon will have realized the opportunity and some of the economics of the result.

I don't think the model is appropriate for every kind of company, but maybe it can work for companies that have large, diverse teams of creative scientists. This model has been terrific for Intrexon. The investors in the fund, I believe, will benefit as well—if all goes as planned.

JOHN CUMBERS: Where do you see the biggest near-term impacts of engineered biology on traditional industries?

tasting

R.J. KIRK: Obviously, the greatest impacts thus far have been in healthcare and food, but we have great aspirations and a lot of effort toward the energy, environment, and consumer industries. While we have very significant achievements in energy and in environment, I think people will be most interested in and excited by our consumer synbio products. I am eager to see them arrive.

Other traditional industries will be seeing impact as well, however. As we become more adept at engineering biology, one major impact will be in the field of materials. Many new materials will be spawned through engineered biology.

Someone recently asked me if Intrexon could help them refine their nylon production. One thing to bear in mind is that the creation of nylon in several ways may represent a defining moment in the history of chemical engineering, but the industrial vector that we want is one of biological engineering. My initial response to the answer was that we, or others probably could improve the industrial process but that's a low value-add proposition. Wouldn't it be more interesting, I suggested, to create another 'nylon moment' using engineered biology?

The world of biology has hundreds of thousands, if not millions, of examples of fiber. Most of them have never been characterized for their properties. We have the technology today to figure out the pathways for most of them. We do not need the entire original organism to produce those fibers. We can already engineer those pathways into microbes at lower costs and produce those fibers at higher volumes than they're made in nature. In addition, we shall see examples of materials that never existed in nature at all but that merely utilize organisms to produce them.   *Silk*

KARL SCHMIEDER: What is the most important thing non-biotech people misunderstand about biotechnology?

R.J. KIRK: I think that most of us fail to appreciate the implications of being biological ourselves and how vast and interconnected the biosphere is. Viewed broadly, biotechnology is merely our coming to terms with our reality, learning how to master the systems that we inherited for the maximum good. Indeed, this is our challenge as well because if we don't do that we shall find ourselves in great trouble.

Learning how to engineer our planet and taking responsibility for our work is not optional.

I am optimistic that we shall acquit ourselves of this charge, however, and so am encouraged. We are seeing a lot of invention and discovery in synthetic biology. The future is going to be very exciting indeed.

SECTION 4. DEVELOPING A BIO STRATEGY

Once a new technology rolls over you, if you're not part of the steamroller, you're part of the road.

—Stewart Brand

EVERY COMPANY IS A BIOLOGY COMPANY

It was only a few short years ago that Peter Sondergaard of the technology research firm Gartner said, "Every company is a technology company." That might have sounded radical in 2013 but two years later, Microsoft CEO Satya Nadella expanded on the idea by saying, "Every business will become a software business, build applications, use advanced analytics and provide Software as a Service services."

Though we now recognize the idea that every company is a technology company as common sense, change was occurring so rapidly we didn't even recognize it until a few years later.

Both quotations speak to the fact that digital technologies have become a part of every company in every industry.

According to the global market intelligence firm IDC, some US$24 trillion was spent globally on information technology in 2016. That's one-third of the estimated US$74 trillion global economy. It's more than the *combined* gross domestic product of China (US$11 trillion), Japan (US$4.4 trillion), Germany (US$3.4 trillion), United Kingdom (US$2.9 trillion), and France (US$2.4 trillion).[61] It's slightly less than the gross domestic product of China and the United States combined (US$29 trillion).[62]

Some say that the digitization of biology will turn every biotechnology company into a software company, especially when you apply artificial intelligence, machine learning, cloud services, automation, and robotics.

But biology is ultimately more complex. As we become experts in engineering biology, we will find it is more powerful and rewarding than digital technologies. It is life. As we mentioned previously, it operates on the microscopic and mega-meter scale.

It will take some time before biology is fully digitized, though eventually its impact will accelerate from biotechnology to all industries. The Wilson Center's Elenore Pauwels noted, "business models that worked in IT or digital are very quickly being transferred to biology."

When it comes to data organization and data storage, information technologies have a lot to learn from biology. Twist Biosciences Emily LeProust pointed out that DNA data storage will become a $10 billion to $15 billion market (of a projected $144 billion market in 2022). In the long-term, biology will impact information technologies in ways we can't imagine.

Before we suggest you need a bio strategy for your company, let's step back to remember that people—living, breathing, thinking advanced forms of biology—started your company, work at your company and buy your products and services. As a result, your company is already a bio company. Every firm is already a living organism with its own systems for survival, environmental resource utilization, and evolution.

Part of change management and preparing for the future is the ability to embrace new opportunities that involve people management and knowledge management, especially in the face of potentially disruptive, exponential change.

As R.J. Kirk pointed out, technophobia may be conserved genetically, but technology always wins. That means biotechnology in all its forms is winning and your bio strategy will depend on people.

Your strategy—whether focused on bio and artificial intelligence, bio-manufacturing, bio-automation, sourcing, pricing, or outsourcing—won't succeed without people to implement it. Emergent strategies won't emerge, much less succeed, if the right people aren't detecting and fostering them.

This requires understanding that people don't resist change (and won't resist your bio strategy) because they are stubborn or political. They'll resist change because they have different perspectives on current realities and future possibilities that must be taken into consideration.

No matter what your business does, the ability to adopt a new technology is key to success whether that technology is artificial intelligence, blockchain, a novel manufacturing method, robotics, or biology.

Mobilizing an organization around a bio strategy requires clear communications and understanding how of biology will positively impact the business.

WHAT IS A BIO STRATEGY?

> At the dawn of the 21st Century, strategy
> seems to have gone out of fashion.
> —Chet Holmes, Certain to Win

The word "strategy" has become so overused that most people have forgotten what strategy really means.

As we mentioned at the beginning of the book, we were inspired to write *What's Your Bio Strategy?* because it was clear that few businesses understood the impact that biology was having—even among those who could benefit from the technologies. After all, the phrase "knowledge is power" is commonly attributed to Francis Bacon, the father of the scientific method and visionary for the first scientific institution, the Royal Society of London for Improving Natural Knowledge.[63]

Before we define bio strategy, let's review what strategy is.

Strategy defines your destination, not the road to get there.

Strategy is a guiding framework.

Strategy, according to Kenichi Ohmrae of McKinsey's Tokyo office, "isn't about beating the competition. It's serving customers' real needs."

Harvard Business School professor Gary Pisano says, "Strategy is nothing more than a commitment to a set of coherent, mutually reinforcing policies aimed at achieving a specific competitive goal. Good strategies promote alignment among diverse groups in an organization, clarify objectives and priorities, and help focus efforts around them."

Martin Reeves, the managing director of Boston Consulting Group's New York office and author of *Your Strategy Needs a Strategy*, suggests that all companies are identical to biological species in that both are complex adaptive systems.[64] Therefore, the strategies that confer the ability to survive and thrive under rapidly changing conditions, whether natural or manmade, are directly applicable to business.

Bio strategy is a framework for incorporating biology into your business.

It is a plan to incorporate biology into your company's existing mission, vision, and goals.

Whether that means using:

- biology to fuel, feed or heal the world,
- genetic engineering to create new foods and fragrances that you've never tasted or smelled, designer materials with novel characteristics, probiotics that clean your teeth while you sleep, or cells that detect and fight cancer,
- computer-aided design tools to create living circuits that can interact with the environment around them, increase the efficiency of bioprocessing, create medicines in your own microbiome, or living sensors that detect changes in the environment,
- cloudlabs or bio-automation technologies that enable entrepreneurs to start new companies on a shoestring,
- gene and genome synthesis tools to rapidly prototype new biological forms or store all the world's data in a DNA-based hard drive the size of a shoebox, or
- creating new opportunities or narratives to engage with customers.

Your bio strategy will guide your use and successful implementation of biotechnology without the need to chase the latest technological fad or be distracted by today's hottest innovation. It's a strategic differentiator that examines internal processes and leverages existing market data to create a competitive advantage.

Your bio strategy should inspire the people in your organization to get excited about the application of biology to solve business-related problems, get them involved in the process, and give them specific goals that will make the strategy work.

Paul Freemont of Imperial College London commented that most big companies do not understand how quickly small companies are innovating, and this should serve as motivation for companies large and small. He also said, "Synthetic biology can have its greatest impact on consumer products that people use every day."

Innovation is a corporate mantra across all industries. Bio strategy is part of that.

Bio strategy is also about organizational transformation—something you will discuss regularly, track progress, review, and calibrate as needed. As Drew Endy said, "If you're not paying attention and preparing your business [for biology] now, it won't be relevant."

Our framework will give you a starting point to develop a bio strategy that fits into your existing business strategy or innovation strategy to match your specific competitive needs.

THE 6 DS OF EXPONENTIAL GROWTH

Peter Diamandis, founder of the X Prize Foundation and Singularity University, and Steven Kotler, founder of the Flow Genome Project, described the growth cycles of exponentially advancing technologies in their book *Bold*. Here are their definitions:

1. **Digitalization:** Once you digitize a product or service (photography, finance, manufacturing, biology) into ones and zeroes, that product or service becomes an information-based technology and hops on an exponential growth curve. We've already witnessed exponential drops in the cost of reading and writing DNA, technologies that are the basis of synthetic biology. As the digitization of biology continues, those prices will continue to drop. Steeply.

2. **Deception:** After initial introduction, some technologies are dismissed by people as irrelevant. During this deceptive growth phase, the technologies advance quickly, often below the radar. The doubling of small numbers seem deceptively flat. In the case

of synthetic biology, we've seen a steady growth in investments made in startups—more than US$1 billion in 2016.

3. **Disruption:** Once refined, these technologies disrupt established industries. Examples typically used include Uber's disruption of the taxi industry and Instagram's disruption of photo sharing. We are in the early stages of synthetic biology disrupting the ingredients industry, with companies using the technology to produce omega-3s, palm oil, squalene, and vanillin.

4. **Demonetization:** Once a product or service has been converted into ones and zeros, the cost of replication and transmission is nearly zero. Digital photography for example, has completely demonetized the field. Consumers no longer need to buy film to take pictures and share images. At a certain point in the near future, the cost of reading and writing DNA will be zero. This will enable the creation of items we can't yet imagine.

5. **Dematerialization:** The concept is that physical tools are replaced by physical and virtual applications. Smartphones, for example, combine a telephone, GPS locator, internet browser, radio, MP3 player, camera, and video recorder. In the 1980s, those technologies purchased separately would have cost more than a million U.S. dollars. We are witnessing the transition from wet labs to digital and cloud labs, where services and science can be readily outsourced.

6. **Democratization:** As costs decrease, access to digital technology becomes available to everyone. As products and services dematerialize and demonetize, they become available to billions of users across the planet. In the 1980s, cellphone use was limited to the very wealthy. It was a luxury. Today, some 3 billion people are connected on planet Earth. That number will increase to 8 billion by 2025. The growth of the International Genetically Engineered Machine (iGEM) Competition is one example of this, thousands of students compete each year to create new bio-based technologies and products. They share their skills and knowledge with their communities, and contribute to BioBricks, the growing registry of standard, interchangeable DNA sequences.

HOW TO DEVELOP A BIO STRATEGY

Sun Tzu starts his classic book on strategy, *The Art of War*, with a chapter on making plans. He states, "Victorious warriors win first, then go to war while defeated warriors go to war, then seek to win."

The current business environment is volatile. Companies are being disrupted every day. The competition is not necessarily in your own industry—competition can come from anywhere. Many industries face advantages that are copied quickly, technology changes, or customers seek alternatives then move on. Thinking that the only competition comes from within your industry is dangerous and limits your ability to anticipate changes and see opportunities.

In most markets, we see industries competing with other industries, business models competing with business models even in the same industry and entirely new categories emerging seemingly daily. Competition can come from anywhere. Substantial threats to a given advantage are likely to arise from a peripheral or non-obvious location.

We based our framework for creating a bio strategy on the engineering design-build-test-learn cycle. Since we believe your bio strategy should be part of a continuous, well-managed process—instead of an episodic and tentative one—we also drew upon ideas from Rita Gunter McGrath's transient competitive strategy and agile project management and design thinking methods.[65]

A general business strategy will provide clear and concise answers to the following four key questions:

1. Where do we compete?
2. What unique value do we bring to win in the marketplace?
3. What resources and capabilities do we have and use?
4. How do we sustain our unique value?

Once those questions are answered, you can move onto creating a bio strategy. For most companies that will mean starting with a list of projects or products that are prioritized based on the potential impact of synthetic biology. From there, you can start brainstorming where to create a bio strategy from first to last.

We recommend involving your team early on. In their book *Sprint*, authors Jake Knapp, John Zeratsky, and Branden Kowitz suggest that by involving more team members in the initial planning, the more they'll champion projects down the road. Plus, when it comes to a new technology, involving your team early on will educate them to the potential the technology offers and allow them to imagine how and where they will apply it.

DESIGN YOUR BIO STRATEGY IN ONE DAY

Jake Knapp of Google Ventures believes you can build a prototype for any huge project in five days.[66] We believe you can create your bio strategy in one day if you start with a prioritized project list and vision for the four-weeks, six months and twelve months after you develop the strategy:

Four weeks: What will you create immediately after defining your bio strategy?

Six months: What is the concrete plan necessary to achieve your vision?

Twelve months: Are you seeing results toward your long-term vision? Have you answered the question, "How will the world have changed for the better because we applied biology?"

This doesn't mean you should not be thinking five or ten or twenty years out—you should. But realistically, you can produce measurable results and change the world for the better in twelve months.

Developing a bio strategy should be fun and challenging. You can start the process by asking big questions using biology as a tool for innovation.

For example: What can you grow with living cells?
The obvious answers will come up, but then the creative ones will follow:

- Living body parts
- A food printer
- Self-healing concrete
- Bridges and highways
- A smartphone
- A skyscraper

Once you've gone through this creative process, you can begin thinking about the areas where your company could apply biology.

It is essential to understand where you already apply biology in your business, then choose the one area where biology or synthetic biology can make an immediate impact.

Ask, where could synthetic biology create 10x growth? Growth that might involve risk but gives you the opportunity to multiply your results significantly? This requires big ideas that if executed and communicated well would inspire your team and make the rest of your industry look like they're not even trying.

There may be more than one area, but the area chosen should be very important to your company. It's the area you'll want to build a bio strategy since it's the biggest opportunity for growth, to secure a supply chain, or engage customers.

Among the questions you could answer are the following:

1. What business objectives does a bio strategy need to support?
2. Can we use biology to strengthen our current business strategy?
3. Can biology disrupt significant cost areas in physical goods?
4. Can we use biology to secure our supply chain? To change a manufacturing process? To distribute our manufacturing? To replace scarce resources?
5. How will biology create value for existing or potential customers?
6. What feature/features can we create with biology that is/are missing in everyone else's product?
7. How can we use biology to push our biggest competitor out of the marketplace?
8. Will innovation with biology allow us to create and capture value now and in the future?
9. Is there an inspiring biology/synthetic biology story that we can tell our customers or partners that we otherwise wouldn't be able to tell?

The main idea here is to identify the biggest opportunity for growth and to define a bio strategy on how you'll bridge the gap from strategy to execution.

BUILD IT WITH BIOLOGY

Before you focus on finalizing and executing your bio strategy, you will want to spend some time focusing on the challenges that will prevent you from reaching your vision.

Remember, synthetic biology is a rapidly advancing field. As Ginkgo Biowork's Jason Kelly pointed out in his interview, "We have biotech foundries that will complete a lab protocol three times cheaper in 2018 than they could in 2017."

With that kind of progress, you and your team will need to ask yourselves:

1. What are our top priorities with biology?
2. What are our threats? Our weaknesses?
3. What aren't we paying attention to that we should be?
4. What changes are we seeing in our industry and outside that we should be paying more attention to?
5. Can we collaborate or co-create with our customers or suppliers?
6. What resources are available to assist in implementing our bio strategy?
7. Should we build this capability ourselves?
8. Can we outsource? Partner?
9. Who can help us make smarter decisions?
10. How will we track our progress?

The traditional approach to biotechnology was to hire the scientists and open a laboratory. That model no longer makes sense when you can partner with an organism engineering company that can help you design a microbe to fulfill your needs or you can outsource your research to a small, focused team that will leverage software and cloudlabs.

John Melo of Amyris, Ginkgo's Kelly, Josh Hoffman of Zymergen, and R.J. Kirk of Intrexon, among others, are part of the growing microbe design industry. Rather than hiring scientists, building your own lab, and trying to recreate the wheel, the economics point to finding the right collaborator to design the microbes, and then produce or scale production.

Partnering with an Amyris, Ginkgo BioWorks, Intrexon or Zymergen is akin to a technology company partnering with Corning, a company that has repeatedly transformed its business and grown new markets during its 160-year history. According to Harvard Business School's Gary Pisano,

> "The company's business strategy focuses on building 'keystone components' that significantly improve the performance of customers' complex system products. To execute this strategy requires Corning remain on the leading edge of glass and materials science so it can solve challenging problems for customers and to discover new applications for its technologies."[67]

It's a model that has been followed and modified by Apple and Google, among others. Given that the tools of biology are dropping, marginal costs for creating products with biology will get cheaper. This is a model that even very small companies can emulate.

The question then becomes do you partner with one of the larger, established companies or one of the emerging smaller companies that will create a custom solution.

If you do decide to build the capability in-house, what can you do to ensure you are future-proofing that laboratory that will build your solution? What kind of expertise will you have in-house? How will you pay attention to developments in the field to make sure your efforts are not disrupted?

TESTING YOUR BIO STRATEGY

When it's successful, your bio strategy should offer such a compelling vision of the future that it inspires and focuses those who hear it. They are compelled to ask about it and move forward.

Though you can develop your bio strategy in days, it might take time to be able to articulate it well. When it's finished, it should require no more than a cup of coffee and ten minutes to test. When you tell or pitch your strategy, watch how it unfolds in real time and how it plays out on the thoughts and feelings of your audience. You'll want to see the story happen in their eyes to study the reaction.

If the audience is hooked, leaning in and listening, and if their eyes are focused as you tell the story, then you know your bio strategy works.

Your bio strategy must be able to grab attention, hold interest, and pay it off by creating a meaningful, emotional experience. If your bio strategy can't work in ten minutes or ten slides, it's won't motivate your team nor your stakeholders. Everything that's wrong in a ten-minute pitch will be ten times worse when you start creating the hour-long presentation decks.

When your bio strategy is so strong it brings silence—no comments, no criticism, just a look of pleasure—that's a hell of a thing and time is too precious to waste on a story that hasn't that power.

Here are some of the questions you'll want to ask when you're testing your bio strategy:

1. What kind of reaction did you receive internally? Externally?
2. What metrics will you define to determine your success or failure?
3. How will you track your progress?
4. How would an outsider view your bio strategy?

LEARNING FROM YOUR BIO STRATEGY

The process ends and begins again with learning.

As Rodrigo Martinez of Veritas Genetics pointed out, learning could be where your company creates a group of pirates to study what biology has to offer your business now and in the future.

After you've created your bio strategy, you will want a clear articulation of specific goals related to helping your company develop a competitive advantage. Here are some of the questions you can ask to help you understand and apply the learnings you get from creating and executing a bio strategy:

1. What did we learn?
2. How can we apply those learnings?
3. Can we scale our learnings?
4. How would biology put us out of business?
5. How did our customers react?
6. Did our message work? How could we improve it?

INTRODUCING THE CHIEF BIOLOGY OFFICER

Twenty years ago, the idea that a company would have a chief digital officer, an executive responsible not only for computer and networking equipment but also for cybersecurity and digital strategy, seemed laughable.

The idea that companies would have a C-level executive focused on computer innovation, creating plans based on new products, assessing the market, looking at new manufacturing techniques and new technologies, was farfetched.

Yet today, both positions are C-level and often occupy a board seat.

General Electric hired a chief digital officer, then added digital officers to each of its many divisions. Those officers report not only to their division heads, but also to the executive chief digital officer.

James Hallinan of Cambridge Consultants introduced us to the concept of the Chief Biology Officer. When we searched for the term in early-2017, we found only two people had the term, Serguei Nabirotchkin, co-founder of Pharnext, and Marc Vasseur, co-founder of GenSet. Both Pharnext and Genset are therapeutics-focused biotechnology companies.

How will that number change in the next ten years?

Although relatively unknown today, the Chief Biology Officer will be responsible for a company's biological efforts. She will arrive having a track record of biological implementations. She will be able to identify future product needs and determine how best to implement and communicate those to others in the organization. Her job will include defining strategies to incorporate biology into the business, to improve and enhance products, secure supply chains, and partner with tools and service providers across all the dimensions of the synthetic biology tool stack.

Like others at the C-level, the chief biology officer will need to be able to drive her vision forward and build and bridge connections, both within the organization and outside.

Even though the title doesn't exist today, we believe it soon will become an essential part of every company the same way the Chief Information and the Chief Digital Officers arrived to transform businesses.

BIOLOGY AS A SERVICE

Predicting the future is no easy feat. We mentioned IBM's Thomas Watson's inability to foresee the spread of computers nor Intel's inability to foresee the rise of smartphones and the internet. More recently, few would have predicted Brexit and Donald Trump's victory.

Experts from the Global Futures Councils have written extensively on how they view the world in 2030. Predictions include the death of shopping and the resurgence of the nation state.

For our purposes, we've chosen to extrapolate on one of their ideas: All products will have become services.

Danish politician and parliament member Ida Auken predicted that in 2030, few of us will own anything—no car, no home, no appliances, no clothes, "...everything you considered a product, has now become a service."[68]

Biotechnology will be no different. Over the next few years, we will see the emergence and rise of Biology as a Service (BaaS).

BaaS doesn't exist today, but the foundational pieces are rapidly being put together.

Companies like GenScript, GeneWiz, Integrated DNA Technologies, Origene, Twist BioSciences, Synthego and others are synthesizing DNA and RNA on demand and are facilitating gene editing. Ginkgo BioWorks and Zymergen are laying the foundation for the microorganism engineering industry. Amyris and others will enable the scaling of production from microliter quantities to commodity quantities. Bolt Threads, Ecovative, and Modern Meadow enable biofabrication. Riffyn and Synthace make it possible to easily transfer digital knowledge from one lab to another.

Though category winners may exercise substantial control for a time, making it difficult for new entrants to dominate a market, new approaches will always be applied and we'll see disruptions as new platforms are created.

Right now, we're building awareness of the possibilities offered by engineered biology and are already in an education phase. Consumer biotechnology products are starting to reach the market.

Over time, as the technologies continue to mature, we expect to see biotechnology firms that solve problems for specific industries, such as agriculture, construction, consumer goods, and biopharmaceuticals.

BaaS will emerge to serve a large and educated customer base, who are aware of the benefits of biology. Competition will increase across the landscape and customers will have many choices among many great products. In some categories, it will be hard to differentiate one product from competitors.

The great news is that now is a great time to develop a bio strategy. Funding across biotechnology is increasing, there are biotech-based consumer applications to create, and biology allows you to tell a great sustainability story. We will see further advances and changes that will allow more businesses to leverage the power of biology.

Relatively speaking, biotechnology is young and the future is bright—even though we know there will be ups and downs. The need for BaaS is only just beginning.

IN CLOSING

We see our bio strategy framework as a living document. We'll update interviews and ask questions across the industry based on the comments and feedback we receive on our website, www.whatsyourbiostrategy.com. We'll be refining the methodology based on the feedback you give us and how it is used in businesses that have implemented it.

We're excited about the possibilities for biology in your business and look forward to staying in touch.

If you want to stay informed of the ideas we present and the evolution of the synthetic biology industry, we invite you to subscribe to the SynBioBeta digest (https://synbiobeta.com/subscribe/), where you can gain insights on the tools, trends, technologies and investments making biology easier to engineer.

Connect with us on Twitter (@johncumbers and @karlschmieder). Send us an email at hello@whatsyourbiostrategy.com and let us know what you've learned and how you've been successful in using bio strategy to transform your company or start a new business.

Also, come visit us at www.whatsyourbiostrategy for free worksheets, downloads, and additional resources.

We're excited about the possibilities for biology in your business and look forward to staying in touch.

Go out, use biology and make the world a better place.

NOTES

INTRODUCTION

1. Rob Carlson, *Biology is Technology*.

2. Rob Carlson, Estimating the Biotech Sector's Contribution to the US Economy. *Nature Biotechnology* (2016). 34: 247–255.

3. Hesseltine CW, Wang HL. The Importance of Traditional Fermented Foods. *BioScience* (1980). 30 (6): 402-404.

4. Enzymes are used in detergents, food and beverage production, and pharmaceuticals. They are used to create paper, biofuels, rubber, contact lens cleaners. They are also essential tools for molecular biology. The enzyme market in 2015, according to Grand View Research, was worth some US$8.18 billion in 2015. Source: Grand View Research <http://www.grandviewresearch.com/industry-analysis/enzymes-industry>.

5. Anthony, S. Kodak's Downfall Wasn't About Technology. *Harvard Business Review*. July 2016. <https://hbr.org/2016/07/kodaks-downfall-wasnt-about-technology>.

6. *Synthetic Biology.org*.

7. *U.K. Royal Society*.

J. CRAIG VENTER: UNDERSTANDING BIOLOGY ALLOWS US TO IMPROVE HUMANITY

8. Senescent cells are damaged cells that stop dividing, accumulate with age, and are thought to contribute to inflammation, tissue damage and age-related diseases.

9. T-cells are white blood cells that are key to the human immune system. T-cells serve soldiers who search out and destroy the targeted invaders.

10. In computer terms, a compiler is a program that translates instruction text into a different language of instruction text. The first language or instruction text is called the source code. The second language, called the target, typically tells the computer what to do. In biology, by analogy, the source code is DNA and the output language is RNA, which is translated into proteins.

11. The Sorcerer is a 2-year scientific expedition that is part of the *Global Ocean Sampling Expedition*, circumnavigating the globe in mid-latitudes collecting samples of microbes in seawater for genetic sequencing and cataloguing. Source: <http://www.jcvi.org/cms/research/projects/gos/overview/>

12. CRISPR, stands for Clustered Regularly Interspaced Short Palindromic Repeats, a genome editing tool that allows scientists to edit genomes with unprecedented precision, efficiency, and flexibility. CRISPR is actually a naturally-occurring bacterial defense mechanism discovered in the 1980s. For more information, visit the resource section at www.whatsyourbiostrategy.com/resources.

PAM SILVER: WE MUST APPROACH SYNTHETIC BIOLOGY SYSTEMATICALLY

13. The International Genetically Engineered Machine (iGEM) competition is a worldwide synthetic biology competition that grew out of courses offered at the Massachusetts Institute of Technology in 2003 and 2004. It en-courages high school and university students to solve real-world challenges by building genetically engineered biological systems. For more information, visit www.igem.org.

PIERRE MONSAN: UNDERSTANDING LIVING SYSTEMS IS MORE IMPORTANT THAN MARS

14. http://www.glowee.eu/

RODRIGO MARTINEZ: IS THE BIOECONOMY IRRELEVANT?

15. Genbank. <https://www.ncbi.nlm.nih.gov/genbank/>.

16. European Nucleotide Archive. <http://www.ebi.ac.U.K./ena>.

17. DNA Data Bank of Japan. <http://www.ddbj.nig.ac.jp/>.

18. Genetic algorithms, according to AI-Junkie.com are a way of solving problems that mimic the same processes hat mother nature uses: selection, recombination, mutation, and evolution. <Source:<http://www.ai-junkie.com/ga/intro/gat1.html>. Genetic algorithms have been used to create computer-aided design tools and applied to solving problems as diverse as aircraft wing design, modeling global temperature change and shipping container loading optimization. Source: <https://www.quora.com/What-are-some-real-world-applications-of-genetic-algorithms>.

PAUL FREEMONT: CREATIVITY IS DRIVING INNOVATION IN SYNTHETIC BIOLOGY

19. Synbicite.com <http://www.synbicite.com/>.

20. The Biodesign Challenge offers art and design students the opportunity to envision future applications of biotechnology. For more information, visit www.biodesignchallenge.org.

21. For more information, visit www.openplant.org.

CHRISTINA AGAPAKIS: THE PRODUCT IS LIFE ITSELF

22. The 100 percent biodegradable Adidas Futurecraft Biofabric sneaker was manufactured from silk polymers supplied by AMSilk, a leading industrial supplier of silk biopolymers.

ROB CARLSON: YOU'LL SOON BE USING SYNTHETIC BIOLOGY TO MANUFACTURE EVERYTHING

23. Biological Technology in 2050. <http://www.synthesis.cc/biological-technology-in-2050/>

24. A New Motorcycle Brand Springs From a Computer. *The Economist.* December 2016. <http://www.economist.com/news/business/21711506-startup-uses-digital-engineering-enter-market-new-motorcycle-brand-springs>.

25. Amyris.com <https://amyris.com/>.

26. Ginkgo Bioworks and Amyris Partner to Accelerate Commercialization of Bio-Based Products. June 2016. Amyris.com <http://investors.amyris.com/releasedetail.cfm?releaseid=977543>.

27. GinkgoBioworks.com. <http://www.ginkgobioworks.com/>.

28. https://www.linkedin.com/in/tsgardner/>.

29. Riffyn.com. <http://riffyn.com/>.

30. GitHub is a software development platform where programmers host, share, and review code, and manage and build projects alongside other programmers. GitHub allows programmers to edit files, see who has changed what, view old versions, with access available from anywhere in the world.

31. Synthace.com. <http://www.synthace.com/>.

32. Zymergen.com. <http://www.zymergen.com/>.

EMILY LEPROUST: ACCELERATING SYNTHESIS OF LIFE'S BUILDING BLOCKS

33. Changing Our Minds. The Leading Global Thinkers of 2015. *Foreign Policy*. 2015. <http://2015globalthinkers.foreignpolicy.com/#moguls/detail/leproust>.

BETHAN WOLFENDEN: SYNTHETIC BIOLOGY'S HARDWARE SHOULD BE ACCESSIBLE

34. The polymerase chain reaction (or PCR) is a laboratory technique used to create many copies of a specific DNA region in vitro. It is sometimes called "molecular photocopying." It is considered one of the most important scientific advances in molecular biology and revolutionized the study of DNA. PCR's creator, Kary B. Mullis, was awarded the Nobel Prize for Chemistry in 1993.

EBEN BAYER: CHICKENS ARE MORE COMPLICATED THAN IPHONES

35. Greenbuild is the world's largest conference dedicated to green building. For more information, visit www.greenbuild.com.

JAY KEASLING: PREPARE FOR THE BIOLOGICAL IPHONE

36. Started in 2006, Synberc is a U.S.-based research program making biology easier to engineer. For more information, visit www.synberc.org.

37. Jef Boeke, Ph.D., is a geneticist and founding director of The Institute for Systems Genetics at NYU Langone Medical Center. Along with George Church and Andrew Hessel, Boeke is leading Genome Project-Write, a project aimed at writing (or synthetizing) large genomes.

38. In 2016, the CRISPR-focused companies CRISPR Therapeutics, Editas Medicine and Intellia went public. CRISPR Therapeutics raised US$56 million. Editas and Intellia each raised more than US$100 million in their offerings.

39. Codon Devices was launched in 2004 by George Church, Drew Endy, Joseph Jacobson and Keasling. The company focused on industrial applications of synthetic biology. The company raised some $44 million in venture capital funding but would close its doors in 2009.

DREW ENDY: THE COMMERCIAL OPPORTUNITIES FOR BIOTECHNOLOGY ARE INFINITE

40. iGEM.org. <http://igem.org/Main_Page>.

41. Biobricks.org, <http://biobricks.org/>.

42. Bionet.io. <http://www.bionet.io/>.

43. Endy, D. Foundations for Engineering Biology. *Nature.* 438, 449-453 (24 November 2005). <http://www.nature.com/nature/journal/v438/n7067/full/nature04342.html>.

44. Molecular Sciences Institute. <http://www.molsci.org/>.

45. 2003 Synthetic Biology Study. Dpsace.MIT.edu. (2003) <http://dspace.mit.edu/handle/1721.1/38455>.

46. Endy, D. Foundations for Engineering Biology. *Nature.* 438, 449-453 (24 November 2005). <http://www.nature.com/nature/journal/v438/n7067/full/nature04342.html>.

47. Blue Heron Bio. <http://www.blueheronbio.com/>.

48. Thodey, K., et al. A microbial biomanufacturing platform for natural and semisynthetic opioids. *Nature Chemical Biology.* 10, 837–844 (2014). <http://www.nature.com/nchembio/journal/v10/n10/full/nchembio.1613.html>.

49. Anthea. <http://antheia.bio/>.

50. Bonnet, J. et al. Amplifying Genetic Logic Gates. *Science* 03 May 2013: Vol. 340, Issue 6132, pp. 599-603. <http://science.sciencemag.org/content/340/6132/599>.

ELEONORE PAUWELS: THE INTERSECTION OF GENOMICS, SYNTHETIC BIOLOGY, ARTIFICIAL INTELLIGENCE, AND SECURITY

51. Gene drives are a genetic-engineering technology that can force the spread of a genetic trait through a population. Typically, a specific trait has a 50-50 chance of being spread from one generation to the next. Gene drives can push that to nearly 100 percent.

52. Oxford Nanopore developed the first and only portable DNA sequencer, the MinION. About the size of a TV remote control, the MinION connects to a computer's USB port.

JOSHUA HOFFMAN: THE RELIABLE OPTIMIZATION OF BIOLOGY CHANGES EVERYTHING

53. Shaping Life in the Lab. *Time Magazine*. March 9, 1981.

JASON KELLY: WE'RE BUILDING THE MICROBE DESIGN INDUSTRY

54. Why the First YC-backed Biotech Company May Just Be the Future of Pharma. *Techcrunch*. 16 July 2014. <https://techcrunch.com/2014/07/16/why-the-first-yc-backed-biotech-company-may-just-be-the-future-of-pharma/>.

55. Kelly, Jason. I run a GMO Company and I support GMO Labeling. *NYTimes*. 15 May, 2016.<https://www.nytimes.com/2016/05/16/opinion/i-run-a-gmo-company-and-i-support-gmo-labeling.html>.

GEORGE CHURCH: WE'LL BE CRISPR GENE-EDITING ADULTS SOON

56. The U.S. Department of Health & Human Services Brain Research through Advancing Innovative Neurotechnologies® (BRAIN) Initiative is aimed at revolutionizing our understanding of the human brain using a number of technologies. For more information visit www.braininitiative.nih.gov.

57. With Stringent Oversight, Heritable Germline Editing Clinical Trials Could One Day Be Permitted for Serious Conditions; Non-Heritable Clinical Trials Should Be Limited to Treating or Preventing Disease or Disability at This Time. The National Academies of Sciences Engineering Medicine. Press release. 14 February 2017. <http://www8.nationalacademies.org/onpinews/newsitem.aspx?RecordID=24623>.

SUZANNE LEE: FUTURE FASHION IS BIOFABRICATED

58. The Biofabricate conference brings together designers and scientists, artists and engineers, global brands and startups, investors and policy makers and trend-forecasters and media. For more information, visit www.biofabricate.co.

ANDREW HESSEL: ENGINEERING LIVING ORGANISMS WILL BE THE WORLD'S BIGGEST INDUSTRY

59. Hessel is referring to the 44th episode of the American science fiction television series, Star Trek. In this 1967 episode, Lieutenant Uhura is given a tribble, a small, furry alien lifeform, with dramatic consequences.

"R.J. KIRK: BIOTECHNOLOGY IS THE GREATEST INDUSTRIAL VECTOR EVER" ON PAGE 147

60. Intrexon CEO Randal J. Kirk Presentation at Borlaug Dialogue International Symposium. *YouTube.com.* <https://www.youtube.com/watch?v=f34bGipU7q8>.

SECTION 4. DEVELOPING A BIO STRATEGY

61. These data are from the International Monetary Fund's World Economic Outlook Database, 2017.

62. According to the International Monetary Fund, the gross domestic product of the United States is some $18 trillion. Source: www.imf.org.

63. It's worth noting that some of the most popular books on strategy today, including *Blue Ocean Strategy*, and Lean and Agile methodologies, ultimately use biology as metaphors.

64. Reeves, Martin. The Biology of Corporate Survival. January-February 2016. *Harvard Business Review.* <https://hbr.org/2016/01/the-biology-of-corporate-survival>.

65. Rita Gunther McGrath. *The End of Competitive Strategy* (Harvard Business Review Press 2013).

66. Knapp, J. From Google Ventures, The 6 Ingredients You Need to Run a Design Sprint. *Fastcodesign.com.* June 6, 2013. <https://www.fastcodesign.com/1672889/from-google-ventures-the-6-ingredients-you-need-to-run-a-design-sprint>.

67. Pisano, G. You Need an Innovation Strategy. *Harvard Business Review,* July 2015. <https://hbr.org/2015/06/you-need-an-innovation-strategy>.

68. Auken, I. Welcome to 2030. I own nothing, have no privacy and life has never been better. *World Economic Forum.* November 2016. <https://www.weforum.org/agenda/2016/11/shopping-i-can-t-really-remember-what-that-is/>.

FOR MORE INFORMATION

Visit <http://www.whatsyourbiostrategy.com/resources/> for a growing list of resources, worksheets, and downloads.

ACKNOWLEDGEMENTS

QUITE A FEW PEOPLE LIVED through this book and encouraged us with their love, kind words, inspiration, support, encouragement, and prodding.

Thanks to the people we interviewed for sharing their time and their stories. You are smart and brilliant and it was an honor to speak with you all. The nature of the interviews should be an inspiration to everyone who reads them. After every interview, we would be punching the air with excitement about the content and stories that we had just heard.

We'd like to thank Franklin Abrams, Marion Cumbers, Erum Azeez Khan, John Garrison and Susan Rensberger for reading drafts of this manuscript and providing extremely helpful comments. Franklin, especially deserves a shout out for marking up early drafts and always being available for late-night phone calls. Marion also deserves special thanks for pointing out many of the places that non-scientists wouldn't understand and for giving the final drafts a very careful read.

John Cumbers: I'd like to thank my wife, Ying, and our two children, Kai and Zhenzhen, for putting up with the late night and early morning Skype calls. I'd like thank my mom (mum!) for her love, support, and proofreading skills. Mostly I'd like to thank my co-author Karl Schmieder. It's no secret that I love conferences and events because I love meeting people and I am dyslexic. I appreciate that Karl was willing to bear the brunt of my dictations and avoidance of the review process. I'd also like to thank Claire Besinio for transcribing hours and hours of interviews, my assistant, Kristin Sorrentino for scheduling them, and our social media expert Marianna Limas for posting them. Finally, thanks to Kate Wildauer for first prodding me to 'go write the book' during the sum-mer of 2016.

Karl Schmieder: For her love, patience and insight, I'd like to thank my wife, Kristen Adamczyk. I'd also like to thank my sons, Alejandro, Tomás, and Felix, for listening to me talk about the people we interviewed, the stories they told us, and the book you are holding in your hand. This book would not have been possible without your support and understanding. You rock! Thanks also Friko Starc for creating an awesome office space to work in and Alice Wu, just because. I'd also like to thank John Cumbers for pushing this book in a different direction than we had originally proposed. I appreciate you serving as taskmaster when I so easily found excuses to avoid writing.

Finally, a shout out to Christina Agapakis of Ginkgo Bioworks for inviting me to visit the Foundry. John and I ran into each other there and that was how this project got started.

ABOUT THE AUTHORS

John Cumbers Ph.D., is the founder of SynBioBeta, an activity hub for synthetic biology startup companies, industry and investors. He is an operating partner at DCVC and runs the DCVC SynBioBeta fund which invests in seed and pre-seed stage companies. He received his Ph.D., in Molecular Biology, Cell Biology, and Biochemistry from Brown University. John holds a master's degree in bioinformatics from the University of Edinburgh in Scotland and an undergraduate degree in computer science from the University of Hull in England. In 2005, he founded the iGEM (International Genetically Engineered Machines competition) team at Brown University, was an iGEM ambassador to China in 2006/2007, and worked at NASA for 7 years in the field of synthetic biology and resource utilization in space. At NASA he led partnerships to bring new technologies to bear on sustainability challenges on Earth and in space. In 2010, John was the recipient of a National Academies Keck Futures Initiative award to hold a workshop on the role that synthetic biology could play in NASA's missions. Find John on LinkedIn, SynBioBeta, and Twitter as @johncumbers.

Karl Schmieder M.S./M.F.A., is an award-winning writer and founder and CEO of messagingLAB, a strategy and marketing communications firm that has worked with life science leaders for the past 15 years. Karl speaks regularly on strategic and communications issues faced by life science and technology startups. He received his master's in biochemistry from UC Riverside and a masters in fine arts in creative writing from the Naropa Institute. He is an active member of Brooklyn's growing synthetic biology community. Karl's writings have been featured in the *Journal of Commercial Biotechnology*, *Life Science Leader*, and the *Silicon Alley Reporter*. Find Karl on LinkedIn, messagingLAB, Twitter as @karlschmieder.

CPSIA information can be obtained
at www.ICGtesting.com
Printed in the USA
LVHW051208301219
642043LV00006B/1046